Target
Get back on track
5

AQA GCSE (9-1)
English Language
Reading

David Grant

P Pearson

Contents

 This workbook has been developed using the Pearson Progression Map and Scale for English.

To find out more about the Progression Scale for English and to see how it relates to indicative GCSE 9–1 grades go to www.pearsonschools.co.uk/ProgressionServices

Helping you to formulate grade predictions, apply interventions and track progress.

Any reference to indicative grades in the Pearson Target Workbooks and Pearson Progression Services is not to be used as an accurate indicator of how a student will be awarded a grade for their GCSE exams.

You have told us that mapping the Steps from the Pearson Progression Maps to indicative grades will make it simpler for you to accumulate the evidence to formulate your own grade predictions, apply any interventions and track student progress. We're really excited about this work and its potential for helping teachers and students. It is, however, important to understand that this mapping is for guidance only to support teachers' own predictions of progress and is not an accurate predictor of grades.

Our Pearson Progression Scale is criterion referenced. If a student can perform a task or demonstrate a skill, we say they are working at a certain Step according to the criteria. Teachers can mark assessments and issue results with reference to these criteria which do not depend on the wider cohort in any given year. For GCSE exams however, all Awarding Organisations set the grade boundaries with reference to the strength of the cohort in any given year. For more information about how this works please visit: https://www.gov.uk/government/news/setting-standards-for-new-gcses-in-2017

①Tackling an unseen text

This unit will help you begin to tackle the unseen texts which you will encounter in your exams. The skills you will build are to:

- check your reading skills have allowed you to understand the text
- identify the key ideas or points the writer wants to get across to the reader
- identify the writer's intention.

In the exam you will face questions like the one below. This is about the text on page 2. This unit will prepare you for questions like this and help you prepare to answer the other questions in your exams.

Exam-style question

Read again the first part of the source from **lines 1–21**.

Choose **four** statements below which are TRUE.

The three key questions in the **skills boosts** will help you tackle an unseen text.

① **How do I make sure I have understood the text?**   ② **How do I identify the key ideas in the text?**   ③ **How do I identify the writer's intentions?**

Read the extract on page 2 from *London Labour and The London Poor*, written by Henry Mayhew and published in four volumes between 1851 and 1861. You will tackle a 19th century non-fiction extract in the Reading section of your Paper 2 exam.

As you read, remember the following: ⊘

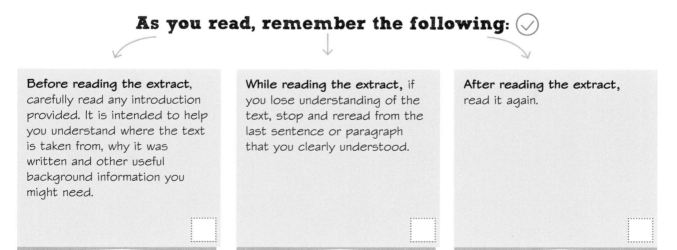

Before reading the extract, carefully read any introduction provided. It is intended to help you understand where the text is taken from, why it was written and other useful background information you might need.

While reading the extract, if you lose understanding of the text, stop and reread from the last sentence or paragraph that you clearly understood.

After reading the extract, read it again.

In this extract from *London Labour and the London Poor*, Henry Mayhew describes the methods used by burglars in Victorian London.

Source 1 London Labour and the London Poor, Henry Mayhew

Breaking into houses, shops, and warehouses is accomplished in various ways, such as picking the locks with skeleton keys; inserting a thin instrument between the sashes and undoing the catch of the windows, which enables the thieves to lift up the under sash; getting over the walls at the back, and breaking open a door or window which is out of sight of the street, or other public place; lifting the cellar-flap or area-grating; getting into
5   an empty house next door, or a few doors off, and passing from the roof to that of the house they intend to rob; entering by an attic window, or trap-door, and if there are neither window nor door on the roof, taking off some of the tiles and entering the house. Sometimes the thieves will make an entry through a brick wall in an adjoining building, or climb the waterspout to get in at the window. These are the general modes of breaking into houses.

Sometimes when doors are fastened with a padlock outside, and no other lock on the door, thieves will get a
10   padlock as near like it as possible. They will then break off the proper lock, one of them will enter the house, and an accomplice will put on a lock as like it as possible to deceive the police, while one or more inside will meantime pack up the goods. Sometimes a well-dressed thief waylays a servant-girl going out on errands in the evening, professes to fall in love with her, and gets into her confidence, till she perhaps admits him into the house when her master and mistress are out. Having confidence in him she shows him over the house, and informs him where
15   the valuables are kept. If the house is well secured, so that there will be difficulty of breaking in by night, he manages to get an accomplice inside to secrete himself till the family has gone to bed, when he admits one or more of his companions into the house. They pack up all they can lay hold of, such as valuables and jewels. On such occasions there is generally one on the outlook outside, who follows the policeman unobserved, and gives the signal to the parties inside when it is safe to come out.

20   In warehouses one of the thieves frequently slips in at closing-time, when only a few servants are left behind, and are busy shutting up. He secretes himself behind goods in the warehouse, and when all have retired for the night, and the door locked, he opens it and lets in his companions to pack up the booty. Should it consist of heavy goods, they generally have a cart to take it away. They are sometimes afraid to engage a cabman unless they can get him to connive at the theft, and, besides, the number of the cab can be taken. They get the goods away in the
25   following manner. If consisting of bulky articles, such as cloth, silks, etc., they fill large bags, similar to sacks, and get as much as they think the cart can conveniently hold, placed near the door. When the policeman has passed by on his round, the watch stationed outside gives the signal; the door is opened, the cart drives up, and four or five sacks are handed into it by two thieves in about a minute, when the vehicle retires.

1 How do I make sure I have understood the text?

It can be tempting to hope that you will fully understand an unseen text once you start answering the questions about it. This page will help you develop strategies to make sure you fully understand the text **before** you answer the questions!

① When you read a new text, you may come across an unfamiliar word or phrase.
You can **either** try to work out its meaning using the rest of the sentence to help you **or** ignore it (if it's not affecting your understanding of the rest of the text).

   a Look at some of the more unusual words from the extract on page 2. Look closely at the sentence in which each one appears. Note down 🖉 what each word or phrase might mean.

      i. sashes (line 2) ....

      ii. cellar-flap (line 4) ....

      iii. modes (line 8) ....

      iv. secrete (line 16) ....

      v. connive (line 24) ....

   b Which words above do you think you could ignore without affecting your understanding of the rest of the text? Mark them with an ⊗.

② When you have read an unseen text once or twice, you should be able to answer these questions:

> **A.** What kind of text is it? Fiction or non-fiction?

> **B.** What's the text about? Can you sum it up in five words or fewer?

> **C.** What's the purpose of the text? To inform, to describe, to argue, or something else?

> **D.** Why do you think the writer decided to write it?

> **E.** Does the writer clearly express or hint at their opinion about the ideas, characters or events in the text? What do you think their opinion is?

Write 🖉 two or three sentences about the extract on page 2. Make sure that your sentences answer all of the questions above. Underline Ⓐ and label 🖉 your writing to show where in your sentences you have answered the questions above.

....

....

....

....

....

....

....

② How do I identify the key ideas in the text?

Identifying the main ideas in a text helps you to:
- improve your understanding of the text as a whole
- explore how and why the text was written.

① One way to gather the main points in a text is to identify the key idea(s) in each paragraph or section of text. You are going to write ✎ a summary of each paragraph in the text on page 2 **using ten words or fewer**.

Carefully read each paragraph and answer the questions in the table below, circling Ⓐ Yes or No.

Write ✎ your summary of each paragraph beneath when you are happy that you have understood its main point(s).

	Paragraph		
	1	2	3
Does the **first** sentence sum up the main point of the paragraph?	Yes / No	Yes / No	Yes / No
Does the **last** sentence sum up the main point of the paragraph?	Yes / No	Yes / No	Yes / No
Can you make any connection between the pieces of information in the paragraph which would effectively sum up its main idea(s)?	Yes / No	Yes / No	Yes / No

Paragraph 1: ....
....

Paragraph 2: ....
....
....

Paragraph 3: ....
....

② Now that you have identified the key points in the text on page 2, you should be able to locate the answers to the questions below quickly and easily.

Exam-style question

List **four** ways in which burglars get into houses.   (4 marks)

1. ....
2. ....
3. ....
4. ....

③ List ✎ two reasons why burglars do not often use a cabman to help them steal heavy goods from warehouses.

1. ....
2. ....

3 How do I identify the writer's intentions?

Your understanding of the writer's intention in a text will guide and support your responses to **all** the questions on the exam.

1 Writers always have an **intention** when they write a text. This could be to influence the reader's:

- actions – to persuade the reader to go and do something
- ideas – to develop the reader's understanding or influence their opinion
- emotions – to make the reader feel a particular way about an idea, event or person.

Write ✏ a sentence or two summing up what you think the writer's intention might be in the extract on page 2.

....

....

....

....

2 One way to help you understand the writer's purpose and intention is to consider whether there is evidence of **bias** in the text. Look at these sentences from the extract on page 2.

> Sometimes a well-dressed thief waylays a servant-girl going out on errands in the evening, professes to fall in love with her, and gets into her confidence, till she perhaps admits him into the house when her master and mistress are out. Having confidence in him she shows him over the house, and informs him where the valuables are kept.

a Can you identify any element of these sentences which reveals the writer's bias? Are they trying to influence your response to:

	Yes	No	✓
the burglars	☐	☐	
their victims	☐	☐	

b If you answered 'Yes' to burglers or victims, what impact do you think the writer wants his opinion to have on the reader? If you answered 'No', why do you think the writer might want the text to appear unbiased? ✏

....

....

....

....

c Look again at the whole extract on page 2. Underline Ⓐ any evidence which suggests that the writer is either biased or unbiased. Write ✏ a short sentence summing up your findings.

....

....

Extracting details from an unseen text

The first question in both your exams tests your skill in extracting information from an unseen text. Once you have read and understood the text fully, and identified the writer's main points, you are ready to tackle this kind of question.

1 Look at one student's answers to the exam-style question and their reasons for choosing them in the thought bubbles below. (The student's answers have been shaded green here.) Do you agree with their answers? Tick ✓ if you do.

Exam-style question

Read again **lines 9–19** of the source.
Choose **four** statements below which are TRUE.

- Shade the boxes of the ones that you think are true.
- Choose a maximum of four statements.

A Burglars use duplicate padlocks to deceive the police that a building is still secure. ▢

B Thieves often start conversations with servant girls they meet in pubs and theatres. ▢

C Thieves may gain a servant girl's confidence by dressing well. This is intended to make the girl think they are honest and respectable. ▢

D Servant girls are usually happy to show thieves him around their masters' houses and tell them where the valuables are kept. ▢

E If a house is difficult to break into, a thief hides in the house and lets others in when everyone has gone to bed. ▢

F A servant is unlikely to allow a stranger into the house when the master or mistress of the house is out. ▢

G Thieves always have someone outside a house they are robbing, looking out for the police. ▢

H The police do not catch burglars very often. ▢

(4 marks)

? A. The writer states this clearly on line 10 so this is definitely **TRUE**.

? B. There is no evidence in these lines to suggest this so it is **NOT TRUE**.

? C. The text does not clearly state this but it does say that a well-dressed thief can gain the girls' confidence so I think I can infer that this is **TRUE**.

? D. The text states that a servant girl might do this if she thinks the thief loves her and she trusts him. So I think this is **NOT TRUE**.

? E. The text says something about an 'accomplice' doing this so I think this is **NOT TRUE**.

? F. The text states that a servant girl might let someone she trusts into the house when her master and mistress are out. This suggests that she wouldn't let a stranger in so I think this is **TRUE**.

? G. The writer says this in the last sentence of the paragraph so I think it is **TRUE**.

? H. There is no evidence in these lines to suggest this so I think it's **NOT TRUE**.

Your turn!

After you have read and understood the text, identified its key points and explored the writer's intention, you are ready to tackle **all of the questions** you are likely to be asked in your exam.

Test yourself with the exam-style question below.

1 Breaking into houses, shops, and warehouses is accomplished in various ways, such as picking the locks with skeleton keys; inserting a thin instrument between the sashes and undoing the catch of the windows, which enables the thieves to lift up the under sash; getting over the walls at the back, and breaking open a door or window which is out of sight of the street, or other public place; lifting the cellar-flap or area-grating; getting into
5 an empty house next door, or a few doors off, and passing from the roof to that of the house they intend to rob; entering by an attic window, or trap-door, and if there are neither window nor door on the roof, taking off some of the tiles and entering the house. Sometimes the thieves will make an entry through a brick wall in an adjoining building, or climb the waterspout to get in at the window. These are the general modes of breaking into houses.

Exam-style question

Read again **lines 1–8** of the source.
Choose **four** statements below which are TRUE.
• Shade the boxes of the ones that you think are true.
• Choose a maximum of four statements.

A Burglars pick the locks of houses with skeleton keys. ☐

B Burglars climb into houses through unlocked windows. ☐

C Burglars can undo the catch on a window from the outside. ☐

D Burglars break in to the back door or window of a house because they are easier to climb through. ☐

E Burglars sometimes get into a cellar and break through the floor above to gain entry to a house. ☐

F Burglars sometimes enter the building next door and make a hole in the brick wall to gain entry to a house that they want to rob. ☐

G Burglars may climb over roofs and remove some of the roof tiles to break into a house they want to rob. ☐

H People should always lock their windows to prevent burglaries. ☐

(4 marks)

Review your skills

Check up

Review your response to the exam-style question on page 7. Tick ✓ the column to show how well you think you have done each of the following.

	Not quite ✓	Nearly there ✓	Got it! ✓
understood the text	☐	☐	☐
identified the key ideas in the text	☐	☐	☐
identified the writer's intention	☐	☐	☐

Look over all of your work in this unit. Note ✏ down the three most important things to remember when you first read an unseen text.

1. ....

2. ....

3. ....

Need more practice?

Here is another exam-style question, this time relating to Source A on page 73: an extract from *The Birds* by Daphne Du Maurier. You'll find some suggested points to refer to in the Answers section.

Exam-style question

Read again the first part of the source, **lines 1 to 11**.

List **four** things from this part of the text that Nat hears. **(4 marks)**

1. ....

2. ....

3. ....

4. ....

How confident do you feel about each of these **skills?** Colour ✏ in the bars.

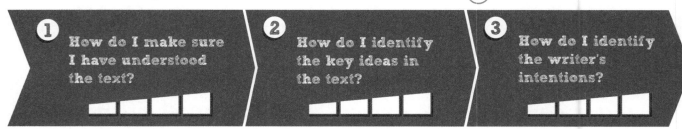

① **How do I make sure I have understood the text?**

② **How do I identify the key ideas in the text?**

③ **How do I identify the writer's intentions?**

Get started

Select and synthesise evidence (AO1)
Explain, comment on and analyse how writers use language and structure to achieve effects and influence readers (AO2)

② Analysing a text

This unit will help you analyse a text, a skill you will need to demonstrate in **all** the longer answers you have to write in your exams. The skills you will build are to:

- select relevant points to make in your analysis
- support your analysis with evidence
- develop your analysis.

In the exam you will face questions like the one below. This is about the text on page 10. At the end of the unit you will write your own response to this question.

Exam-style question

Look in detail at **lines 12 to 23** of the source.

How does the writer use language here to describe the baby?

You could include the writer's choice of:

- words and phrases
- language features and techniques
- sentence forms.

(8 marks)

The three key questions in the **skills boosts** will help you analyse the text.

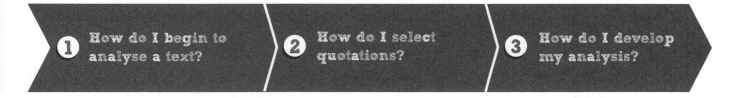

① **How do I begin to analyse a text?**   ② **How do I select quotations?**   ③ **How do I develop my analysis?**

Read the extract on page 10 from *The Fifth Child* by Doris Lessing, published in 1988. You will tackle a 20th century fiction extract in the Reading section of your Paper 1 exam.

As you read, remember the following: ✓

Remember the focus of the exam question you are preparing to respond to. Think about how you respond to the writer's description of the baby.

Think about the ways in which the writer tries to interest and engage readers.

Underline Ⓐ or tick ✓ any parts of the text that you find engaging or interesting.

Harriet and David are expecting their fifth child. Harriet's mother, Dorothy, has been helping her with their four older children.

Source 1 The Fifth Child, Doris Lessing

Soon, nearly a month early, the pains began. Once she started, labour had always gone quickly. Dorothy rang David in London, and at once took Harriet into hospital. For the first time, Harriet had insisted on a hospital, surprising everyone.

By the time she was there, there were strong wrenching pains, worse, she knew, than ever in the past. The baby
5   seemed to be fighting its way out. She was bruised – she knew it; inside she must be one enormous black bruise … and no one would ever know.

When at last the moment came when she could be given oblivion, she cried out, 'Thank God, thank God, it's over at last!' She heard a nurse saying, 'This one's a real little toughie, look at him.' Then a woman's voice was saying, 'Mrs Lovatt, Mrs Lovatt, are you with us? Come back to us! Your husband is here, dear. You've a healthy boy.'

10   'A real little wrestler,' said Dr Brett. 'He came out fighting the whole world.'

She raised herself with difficulty, because the lower half of her body was too sore to move. The baby was put into her arms. Eleven pounds of him. The others had not been more than seven pounds. He was muscular, yellowish, long. It seemed as if he were trying to stand up, pushing his feet into her side.

'He's a funny little chap,' said David, and he sounded dismayed.

15   He was not a pretty baby. He did not look like a baby at all. He had a heavy-shouldered hunched look, as if he were crouching there as he lay. His forehead sloped from his eyes to his crown. His hair grew in an unusual pattern from the double crown where started a wedge or triangle that came low on the forehead, the hair lying forward in a thick yellowish stubble, while the side and back hair grew downwards. His hands were thick and heavy, with pads of muscle in the palms. He opened his eyes and looked straight up into his mother's face. They were focused
20   greeny-yellow eyes, like lumps of **soapstone**. She had been waiting to exchange looks with the creature who, she had been sure, had been trying to hurt her, but there was no recognition there. And her heart contracted with pity for him: poor little beast, his mother disliking him so much … But she heard herself say nervously, though she tried to laugh, 'He's like a troll, or a goblin or something.' And she cuddled him, to make up. But he was stiff and heavy.

25   He was not crying. Harriet held him out, challenging the nurse with her eyes to take him. The nurse, mouth tight with disapproval, took the baby, and he was put unprotesting in his cot. He had not cried since he was born, except for a first roar of protest, or perhaps surprise. The four children were brought in to see their new brother in the hospital ward.

David stood at the end of the bed, holding baby Paul. Harriet yearned for this baby, this little child, from whom
30   she had been separated so soon. She loved the look of him, the comical soft little face, with soft blue eyes - like bluebells, she thought - and his soft little limbs … it was as if she were sliding her hands along them, and then enclosing his feet in her palms. A real baby, a real little child.

soapstone: a soft stone, greenish white in colour

How do I begin to analyse a text?

When you begin to analyse a text, you need to identify those parts of the text which will help you to respond to the question you are answering. When you have done that, you can begin to select quotations to support your choices.

Look again at the exam-style question you are exploring.

Exam-style question

Look in detail at <u>lines 12 to 23</u> of the source.

How does the writer use language here to <u>describe the baby?</u>

① Which of these sections of the extract from lines <u>12 to 23</u> do **you** find most effective in <u>describing the baby?</u> Give each one a mark between 0 and 5, with 0 being not very engaging or interesting and 5 being very engaging and interesting.

	🖉	✓
The baby was put into her arms. Eleven pounds of him. The others had not been more than seven pounds.		
He was muscular, yellowish, long. It seemed as if he were trying to stand up, pushing his feet into her side.		
'He's a funny little chap,' said David, and he sounded dismayed.		
He was not a pretty baby. He did not look like a baby at all.		
He had a heavy-shouldered hunched look, as if he were crouching there as he lay.		
His forehead sloped from his eyes to his crown.		
His hair grew in an unusual pattern from the double crown where started a wedge or triangle that came low on the forehead, the hair lying forward in a thick yellowish stubble, while the side and back hair grew downwards.		
His hands were thick and heavy, with pads of muscle in the palms.		
He opened his eyes and looked straight up into his mother's face. They were focused greeny-yellow eyes, like lumps of soapstone.		

② Look again at your answers to question ① above.

Tick ✓ the **three** sections of the text which you have given the highest score.

For each section you have chosen, Ⓐ underline the part of that element which would make an effective quotation to show how the writer uses language to describe the baby.

2 How do I select quotations?

To help you select the most effective quotations, you need to ask yourself some key questions.

Look again at the exam-style question.

Exam-style question

How does the writer use language here to describe the baby?

(1) Now look at this quotation from the text which you could use in your analysis. Answer the questions (A–D) around it. 🖉

> **A. Can I answer most or all of questions B, C and D?**
>
> If not, choose a different quotation which will help you answer the question.

> **B. Which words or language features in the quotation has the writer used to create some kind of impact?**
>
> Do these words work together to create an impact? Or do they create different effects?

> He was not a pretty baby.
> He did not look like a baby at all.

> **C. What do you notice about the sentence structure(s) in the quotation?**
>
> Are the sentences in the quotation structured as a series of clauses, as short dramatic statements, or something else? What effect does this have?

> **D. What impact does the writer want these choices to have on the reader?**
>
> How do these choices help to describe the baby?

(2) Choose another quotation **from lines 12 to 23** of the extract on page 10: one which will allow you to comment on the writer's choices and their impact on the reader. Annotate 🖉 your chosen quotation with your comments on paper, using questions B to D to help you.

3 How do I develop my analysis?

When you focus on a quotation you have selected, you should aim to make your comments as detailed and specific as you can. Think about:

- commenting on the writer's choice of vocabulary and language features
- commenting on the writer's choice of sentence structure
- being precise about the impact of the writer's choices on the reader.

1 Look closely at this quotation from the extract on page 10.

> He was muscular, yellowish, long. It seemed as if he were trying to stand up, pushing his feet into her side.

Now look at three different students' comments on the ways in which the writer uses language to describe the baby in the quotation above. Annotate 🖊 each comment, identifying:

- what is effective about the analysis
- what could be added or improved.

Student A:

> The baby sounds really strange because of the way the writer describes him. He looks really strange and not like you would expect a baby to look or behave so it makes me think that maybe there is something weird about him.

Student B:

> The word 'yellowish' makes the baby sound unhealthy.

Student C:

> The writer creates a shocking impression of the baby using a short sentence and a list of three adjectives to suggest a weirdly tall, strong, almost non-human baby.

2 Tick ✓ the student's comment above which you think makes the most effective analysis of the quotation. What has the writer of your chosen comment done well? Note down 🖊 three things that you think make it the most successful analysis.

a ....

b ....

c ....

3 Using your answers to question **2** to help you, write 🖊 a sentence or two analysing how the writer uses language to describe the baby in this quotation.

> The baby was put into her arms. Eleven pounds of him.

....

....

....

....

....

Analysing a text

To write an effective analysis you need to do the following.

- Focus closely on the key words in the question: what are you being asked to analyse?
- Identify relevant parts of the text which will help you answer the question.
- Select quotations from those parts of the text, making sure you can comment on them in detail.
- Develop your analysis of each quotation as fully and precisely as possible.

Look at the exam-style question.

Exam-style question

Look in detail at this extract from **lines 12 to 23** of the source.

How does the writer use language here to <u>describe the baby</u>?

(1) Look at this paragraph from one student's response to the exam-style question above.
Link ✐ the annotations to the paragraph to show where the student has used each element of a successful paragraph of analysis.

quotation from the text

The description of the baby is very disturbing and even shocking for readers. The writer emphasises this in the father's reaction to the baby: ''He's a funny little chap,' said David, and he sounded dismayed.' The writer uses this reaction to create tension. The word 'dismayed' suggests his disappointment. The phrase 'funny little chap' does not really sum up the baby described in the rest of the extract so it suggests this short sentence is the only thing the father can think of to say about him. It shows the tense silence in the room as the husband and wife look in shock at their baby.

comments on vocabulary and/or sentence structure choices

comments precisely on the impact of these choices on readers

use key words from the question

(2) One way to structure a paragraph of analysis is to write it in three parts: point/evidence/explain. This writer has included all three elements, but not in that order. Is it effective?
Write ✐ a sentence or two explaining your ideas.

....

....

....

....

....

....

Your turn!

You are now going to write ✏ your own answer in response to the exam-style question.

Exam-style question

Look in detail at this extract from **lines 12 to 23** of the source.

> The baby was put into her arms. Eleven pounds of him. The others had not been more than seven pounds. He was muscular, yellowish, long. It seemed as if he were trying to stand up, pushing his feet into her side.
>
> 'He's a funny little chap,' said David, and he sounded dismayed.
>
> He was not a pretty baby. He did not look like a baby at all. He had a heavy-shouldered hunched look, as if he were crouching there as he lay. His forehead sloped from his eyes to his crown. His hair grew in an unusual pattern from the double crown where started a wedge or triangle that came low on the forehead, the hair lying forward in a thick yellowish stubble, while the side and back hair grew downwards. His hands were thick and heavy, with pads of muscle in the palms. He opened his eyes and looked straight up into his mother's face. They were focused greeny-yellow eyes, like lumps of soapstone.

How does the writer use language here to describe the baby?

You could include the writer's choice of:

- words and phrases
- language features and techniques
- sentence forms.

(8 marks)

① You should spend around 15 minutes on this type of question, so should aim to write three paragraphs.

   a Underline Ⓐ **three** quotations in the extract above which you could focus on in your answer. Remember to choose quotations which will give you opportunities to:

- analyse how the writer engages and interests readers
- analyse the impact of the writer's vocabulary and sentence structure choices
- explore the precise impact of those choices on readers.

   b Annotate ✏ the vocabulary and/or sentence structure choices in your chosen quotations. If you find it tricky to annotate any of them, ask yourself:

- Have I chosen a good quotation?
- Are there better quotations which I could analyse more fully? If so, choose again.

② Write ✏ your response to the exam-style question above on paper.

Review your skills

Check up

Review your response to the exam-style question on page 15. Tick ✓ the column to show how well you think you have done each of the following.

	Had a go ✓	Nearly there ✓	Got it! ✓
identified relevant parts of the text	☐	☐	☐
selected quotations	☐	☐	☐
analysed chosen quotations	☐	☐	☐
focused analysis on the keywords in the question	☐	☐	☐

Look over all of your work in this unit. Note down ✐ the three most important things to remember when you first read an unseen text.

1. ....

2. ....

3. ....

Need more practice?

Here is another exam-style question, this time relating to Source B on page 74: an extract from *The Private Diary of the Master of a London Ragged School*. You'll find some suggested points to refer to in the Answers section.

Exam-style question

Look in more detail at **lines 14 to 32** of the source.

How does the writer use language to create an impression of the students in his school?

You could include the writer's choice of:
- words and phrases
- language features and techniques
- sentence forms.

(8 marks)

How confident do you feel about each of these **skills?** Colour ✐ in the bars.

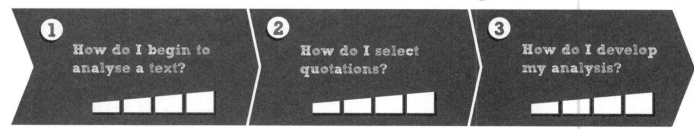

① **How do I begin to analyse a text?**

② **How do I select quotations?**

③ **How do I develop my analysis?**

Get started

Explain, comment on and analyse how writers use language and structure to achieve effects and influence readers (AO2)

③ Commenting on words, phrases and language features

This unit will help you learn how to analyse a writer's use of words, phrases and language features. The skills you will build are to:

- identify significant vocabulary choices in a text
- explore how the writer's vocabulary choices support the writer's intention
- analyse the impact of the writer's choices of words, phrases and language features.

In the exam you will face questions like the one below. This is about the text on page 18. This unit will prepare you to write your own response to this question, focusing on the writer's use of words, phrases and language features. Unit 4 focuses on how to analyse the writer's use of sentence forms.

Exam-style question

Look in detail at **lines 1 to 20** of the source.

How does the writer use language to describe the narrator's thoughts and feelings?

The three key questions in the **skills boosts** will help you comment on language.

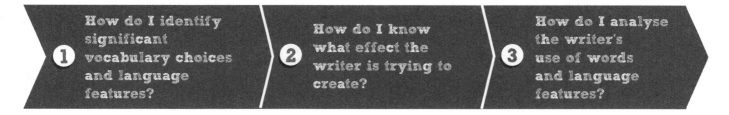

1. How do I identify significant vocabulary choices and language features?

2. How do I know what effect the writer is trying to create?

3. How do I analyse the writer's use of words and language features?

Read the extract on page 18 from *Cider with Rosie*, the first volume of Laurie Lee's autobiography, written in 1959. You will tackle a 20th or 21st century non-fiction extract in the Reading section of your Paper 2 exam.

As you read, remember the following: ⊘

The impression which the writer is trying to create of the narrator and his surroundings in the extract.

Any use of words, phrases or language features in the extract which you find surprising or effective. Annotate 🖉 the text as you find these.

In 1918, Laurie Lee and his family moved from a large town to a small village in the Gloucestershire countryside.

Source 1 Cider with Rosie, Laurie Lee

I was set down from the carrier's cart at the age of three; and there with a sense of bewilderment and terror my life in the village began.

The June grass, amongst which I stood, was taller than I was, and I wept. I had never been so close to grass before. It towered above me and all around me, each blade tattooed with tiger-skins of sunlight. It was knife-edged, dark,
5 and a wicked green, thick as a forest and alive with grasshoppers that chirped and chattered and leapt through the air like monkeys.

I was lost and didn't know where to move. A tropic heat oozed up from the ground, rank with sharp odours of roots and nettles. Snow-clouds of elder-blossom banked in the sky, showering upon me the fumes and flakes of their sweet and giddy suffocation. High overhead ran frenzied larks, screaming, as though the sky were tearing apart.

10 For the first time in my life I was out of the sight of humans. For the first time in my life I was alone in a world whose behaviour I could neither predict nor fathom: a world of birds that squealed, of plants that stank, of insects that sprang about without warning. I was lost and I did not expect to be found again. I put back my head and howled, and the sun hit me smartly on the face, like a bully.

From this daylight nightmare I was awakened, as from many another, by the appearance of my sisters. They came
15 scrambling and calling up the steep rough bank, and parting the long grass found me. Faces of rose, familiar, living; huge shining faces hung up like shields between me and the sky; faces with grins and white teeth (some broken) to be conjured up like genii with a howl, brushing off terror with their broad scoldings and affection. They leaned over me – one, two, three – their mouths smeared with red currants and their hands dripping with juice.

'There, there, it's all right, don't you wail any more. Come down 'ome and we'll stuff you with currants.'

20 And Marjorie, the eldest, lifted me into her long brown hair, and ran me jogging down the path and through the steep rose-filled garden, and set me down on the cottage doorstep, which was our home, though I couldn't believe it.

That was the day we came to the village, in the summer of the last year of the First World War. To a cottage that stood in a half-acre of garden on a steep bank above a lake; a cottage with three floors and a cellar and a treasure
25 in the walls, with a pump and apple trees, syringa and strawberries, rooks in the chimneys, frogs in the cellar, mushrooms on the ceiling, and all for three and sixpence a week.

I don't know where I lived before then. My life began on the carrier's cart which brought me up the long slow hills to the village, and dumped me in the high grass, and lost me. I had ridden wrapped up in a Union Jack to protect me from the sun, and when I rolled out of it, and stood piping loud among the buzzing jungle of that summer
30 bank, then, I feel, was I born. And to all the rest of us, the whole family of eight, it was the beginning of a life.

How do I identify significant vocabulary choices and language features?

In order to identify significant vocabulary choices in a text, focus on the writer's intention and any key words in the question you are answering. For example, in the question shown here, you need to think about the following questions.

- What impression does the writer want to create of the narrator's thoughts and feelings?
- Which parts of the extract show those thoughts and feelings most clearly?

1. Re-read the first two paragraphs of the extract on page 18. How would you sum up the narrator's feelings in these paragraphs in just one or two words?

....

2. Now look at these quotations from the first three paragraphs. Which **two** most clearly show how the narrator is feeling? Tick ✓ your choices.

1.	I was set down from the carrier's cart at the age of three;	☐
2.	there with a sense of bewilderment and terror my life in the village began.	☐
3.	The June grass, amongst which I stood, was taller than I was, and I wept.	☐
4.	I had never been so close to grass before.	☐
5.	It towered above me and all around me, each blade tattooed with tiger-skins of sunlight.	☐
6.	It was knife-edged, dark, and a wicked green, thick as a forest	☐
7.	alive with grasshoppers that chirped and chattered and leapt through the air like monkeys.	☐

3. Look again at your answers to question 2.

   a. In the quotations you chose, circle Ⓐ any words or phrases which show or suggest the narrator's feelings.

   b. Annotate your chosen words or phrases to explain why you chose them.

4. Identify **two** words, phrases or language features in lines 3–10 of the extract that show the narrator's thoughts and feelings. You do not need to explain your choices.

....

....

....

....

Unit 3 Commenting on words, phrases and language features   **19**

2 How do I know what effect the writer is trying to create?

When you think about an effect that the writer is using words, phrases or language features to create, you first need to ask yourself: What is the writer's intention in this text? How are they trying to make me think or feel or react to their ideas?

Look closely at this paragraph from the extract.

> For the first time in my life I was out of the sight of humans. For the first time in my life I was alone in a world whose behaviour I could neither predict nor fathom: a world of birds that squealed, of plants that stank, of insects that sprang about without warning. I was lost and I did not expect to be found again. I put back my head and howled, and the sun hit me smartly on the face, like a bully.

(1) How does the **narrator** feel in this paragraph? Tick ✓ two words from the suggestions below.

| frightened | | intimidated | | abandoned | | confused | |

| threatened | | upset | | angry | | sad | | miserable | |

(2) **a** How do you think the writer wants the **reader** to think and feel as they read this paragraph? Tick ✓ one word from the suggestions below.

| humour | | fear | | tension | | curiosity | | terror | |

| sympathy | | anger | | **antipathy** | | disgust | |

antipathy: the opposite of sympathy: to dislike or feel hostility

b Which parts of the paragraph are most likely to make the reader think or feel that way? Underline Ⓐ two or three words or phrases or sentences in the paragraph above which help the writer to achieve that response.

c Write ✐ a sentence or two explaining your choices in question **b** .

....

....

....

....

(3) Now look at the rest of the extract on page 18. Note down ✐ one or two words in answer to each of these questions:

a How do the writer's feelings change as the extract develops?   ....

b How does the writer want the reader to think and feel as the extract develops?   ....

c Which of the writer's choices of words, phrases or language features help the writer to achieve that response?   ....

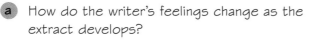

③ How do I analyse the writer's use of words and language features?

You can analyse the writer's use of words, phrases and language features more closely by thinking about the ideas and associations that the writer's vocabulary choices create in the reader's mind. These are called their **connotations**. For example:

The writer describes 'plants that stank'.

Meaning	Connotations	Effect
they smelt	terrible, rotten smell	suggests an uninviting, unpleasant situation

① Look at this sentence from the extract on page 18.

> I put back my head and howled, and the sun hit me smartly on the face, like a bully.

Think about the connotations of the word 'howled'.

a What creature do you expect to 'howl'? 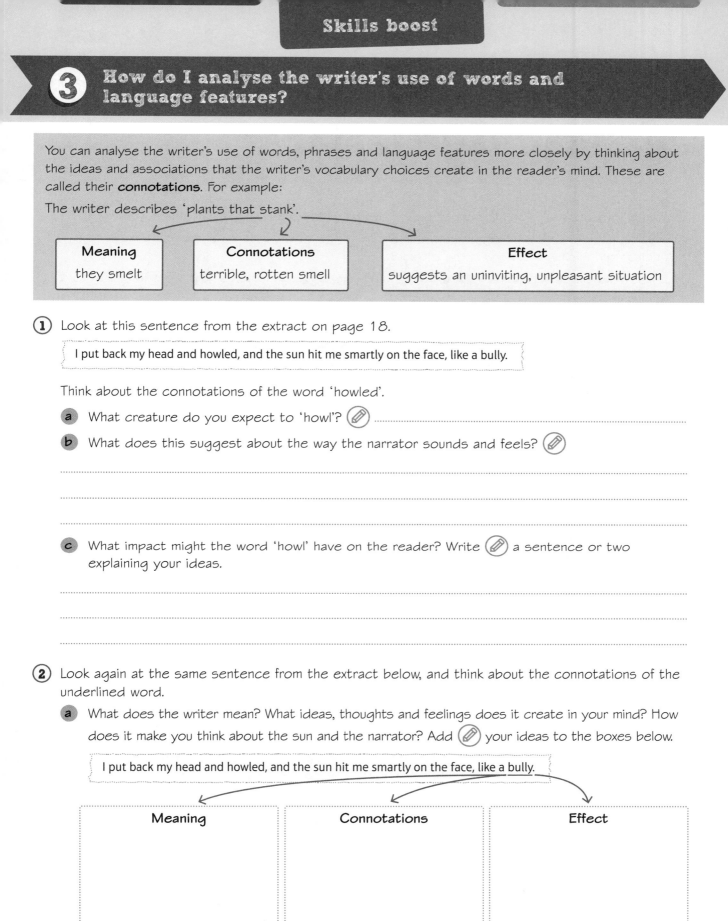 ....

b What does this suggest about the way the narrator sounds and feels?

....

....

....

c What impact might the word 'howl' have on the reader? Write a sentence or two explaining your ideas.

....

....

....

② Look again at the same sentence from the extract below, and think about the connotations of the underlined word.

a What does the writer mean? What ideas, thoughts and feelings does it create in your mind? How does it make you think about the sun and the narrator? Add your ideas to the boxes below.

> I put back my head and howled, and the sun hit me smartly on the face, like a bully.

Meaning	Connotations	Effect

b What impact might the word 'bully' have on the reader? Write a sentence or two explaining your ideas.

....

....

Commenting on words, phrases and language features

To write an effective analysis of the writer's use of words, phrases and language features, you need to:

- think about the writer's different intentions in the text: how does he want the reader to respond to the ideas and events described in the extract?
- consider how the writer's choices of words, phrases and language features help the writer to achieve those intentions.
- analyse in detail the connotations and impact of some of the writer's most significant choices in the extract.

Look at this exam-style question:

Exam-style question

Look in detail at **lines 1 to 20** of the source.

How does the writer use language to describe the narrator's thoughts and feelings?

(1) Carefully re-read the exam-style question above. Circle Ⓐ the **key words in the question**: those words which **either** tell you what you are being asked to do **or** you should include in every paragraph of your answer **or** both.

(2) Now look at a paragraph from one student's response to the question:

uses key words from the question

identifies the writer's intention

supported with evidence from the text

> The writer describes how upset and threatened the narrator feels when he thinks he has been abandoned and will never see his family again. He describes how the narrator is surrounded by grass: 'It was knife-edged, dark, and a wicked green'. The word 'knife-edged' makes it sound sharp and dangerous and threatening and the word 'wicked' makes it sound evil and like it is trying to harm him. The writer uses language to make the reader feel sorry for the narrator because he is so young and he thinks he is in serious danger.

comments on connotations of words and phrases

comments on how this helps to achieve the writer's intention

Can you identify all the different things the student has included in this paragraph?

Link  the annotations to the paragraph to show where the student has included them.

Your turn!

You are now going to plan and write your own answer, focusing on the writer's use of language. (Unit 4 focuses on how to analyse the writer's use of sentence forms.)

Exam-style question

Look in detail at **lines 1 to 20** of the source.

How does the writer use language to describe the narrator's thoughts and feelings?

(1) Think about the ways in which the writer uses language to describe the narrator's thoughts and feelings **in lines 1 to 20**. Note down ✐ three or four ways he does this. Use these sentence starters to help you.

> The writer describes how the narrator feels...
>
> when he...   by including details of...   by writing about...

....

....

....

....

(2) Identify where in the text the writer does each of these things. Note down ✐ some key words, phrases or language features that help the writer to achieve these things.

....

....

....

....

(3) Note down ✐ some ideas which will help you analyse the writer's language choices. How do the connotations of each word or phrase contribute to the writer's intentions? Use the sentence starter ideas to help you.

| This suggests... | This has connotations of... |

| This creates the impression of... | This encourages the reader to feel... |

....

....

....

....

(4) Use your ideas and planning above to write ✐ your response to the exam-style question above on paper.

Review your skills

Check up

Review your response to the exam-style question on page 23. Tick ✓ the column to show how well you think you have done each of the following.

	Had a go ✓	Nearly there ✓	Got it! ✓
identified significant language choices in the text	☐	☐	☐
explored how the writer's language choices support the writer's intention	☐	☐	☐
analysed the impact of the writer's language choices	☐	☐	☐

Look over all of your work in this unit. Note ✎ down the three most important things to remember when analysing the writer's use of words, phrases and language features.

1. ....

2. ....

3. ....

Need more practice?

Here is another exam-style question, this time relating to the extract from Source A on page 73, an extract from *The Birds* by Daphne Du Maurier. You'll find some suggested points to refer to in the Answers section.

Exam-style question

Look in detail at **lines 14 to 23** of the source.

How does the writer use language here to create a tense, frightening atmosphere?

You could include the writer's choice of:
- words and phrases
- language features and techniques
- sentence forms.

(8 marks)

How confident do you feel about each of these **skills?** Colour ✎ in the bars.

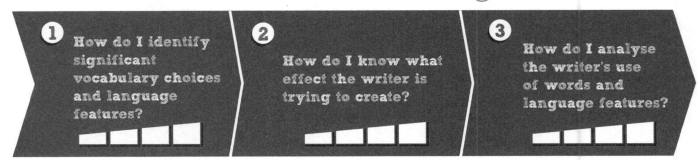

1 How do I identify significant vocabulary choices and language features?

2 How do I know what effect the writer is trying to create?

3 How do I analyse the writer's use of words and language features?

(4) Commenting on sentence forms

This unit will help you comment on sentence forms. The skills you will build are to:

- identify significant choices of sentence form
- comment in detail on the writer's choices of sentence form and their impact
- develop your analysis of the cumulative impact of sentence forms and other language choices.

In the exam you will face questions like the one below. This is about the text on page 26. At the end of the unit you will write your own response to this question, focusing on the writer's use of sentence forms. Unit 3 focuses on how to analyse the writer's use of words, phrases and language features.

Exam-style question

You need to refer **only** to **Source 1** on how to survive the exam season.

How does the writer use language to make you, the reader, understand the experience of facing GCSE exams?

(12 marks)

The three key questions in the **skills boosts** will help you comment on structure.

1 How do I identify sentence form choices that create a specific effect?

2 How do I comment on the writer's use of sentence forms?

3 How do I comment on sentence forms and other language choices?

Read the extract on page 26 from a newspaper article published in 2015. You will tackle a 20th or 21st century non-fiction extract in the Reading section of your Paper 2 exam.

As you read, remember the following:

The ideas and opinions that the writer has selected to describe the experience of facing GCSE exams.

How the writer has structured her sentences to add impact to those ideas and opinions.

This newspaper article appeared in the Guardian in May 2015.

Source 1 How to survive the exam season, Nell Frizzell

All over the country this month, GCSE pupils will be sitting down, once again, to slog through their exams. Whether it's the chorus of sniffing, the three hours of cramping fingers, the coldly sweating armpits or the hotly anticipated questions that never appear, exams are an **archetypal stress dream** for a reason. But I'm afraid they matter. They matter enormously.

5　But exams can also be a brilliant, concise, exciting time to show off your knowledge and make the most of your revision. It's a hoop, sure, but you might as well jump through it with grace. So, as GCSE season hits, here's my guide to surviving, even enjoying, exams.

1. This is not a trick

The first thing to remember with exams, is that they are a test, not a trick. This is your opportunity to show what

10　you know, not to be punished for what you don't.

Walking into an exam with that sort of positive attitude will not only help you make the most of the opportunity, it will also make you much less likely to feel nauseous before the papers have even been handed out.

2. If it works, then work it

I knew a boy who came to his AS-level maths exam wearing a white lab coat, simply because it made him feel

15　cleverer. A boy in a friend's science GCSE exam wore a pair of earplugs to muffle the maddening soundtrack of ticking clocks, sniffing classmates, squeaking chairs and sobbing companions. As a child I went into my English Sats exam clutching a small toy chicken in my sweaty little hand, after my mother told me it was a good luck token.

Exams are not the time for peer pressure. It is perfectly acceptable to admit that you've done some revision [and]

20　it is fine to wear your lucky underwear.

3. Adrenaline is your friend

As it happens, I was good at exams. Even without my lucky chicken. Because, basically, I love adrenaline. The rush of adrenaline as you're told to turn over your papers, the tingling in your feet as you walk up a row of empty wooden desks, the thump of your heart as the stopclock starts and the cold wash of nerves that floods your

25　stomach as you read through that first question are all your body's way of preparing to perform. And an exam is a performance.

Don't be scared of adrenaline, don't dread the rush of nerves; both are essential if you're going to write for an hour or remember the third row of the periodic table.

4. Everybody fails sometimes

30　Einstein had to re-sit his university entrance exam. I'm not saying that flunking exams is a failsafe route to fame, success and an understanding of intermolecular forces; but it doesn't necessarily mean the end of your career.

Retakes exist for a reason and, as anyone learning to kiss can tell you, you'll learn a lot from a failed attempt. Of course you should stay in, get plenty of sleep, eat a healthy breakfast and leave yourself plenty of time to get to the exam. But if things don't all go to plan, if you do spend the exam staring blank-brained at an empty page, then

35　at least your ability to recover will stand you in good stead for years, if not decades to come.

Good luck!

archetypal stress dream: typical of the kind of dream you have when feeling anxious or stressed

1 How do I identify sentence form choices that create a specific effect?

To deliver information clearly, writers often choose to use sentences that are not too short and not too long, often beginning with a noun, noun phrase or pronoun followed by a verb. For example:

> I knew a boy who came to his AS-level maths exam

> A boy in a friend's science GCSE exam wore a pair of earplugs

However, some sentences are also structured to create impact and to help the writer achieve their intention.

1. To identify sentences that may have been crafted for effect rather than clarity, you could look out for sentences:

   A. that are much shorter than most

   B. that are much longer than most

   C. that do not begin with a noun, noun phrase or pronoun

   D. in which a key idea is delayed to the end of the sentence.

   Look at the first paragraph of the article on page 26. Identify one of each of the above types of sentence, annotating them A–D ✎.

2. Look carefully again at this sentence from the article:

   > All over the country this month, GCSE pupils will be sitting down, once again, to slog through their exams.

   The same meaning can be expressed in a completely different sentence structure:

   | once again, | this month, | all over the country, | GCSE pupils will be sitting down | to slog through their exams. |

   a Which of the ideas in the original version is most **strongly** emphasised? Tick ✓ one:

   ☐ people 'all over the country' take GCSEs

   ☐ people are taking GCSEs 'once again'

   ☐ people are taking GCSEs 'this month'

   ☐ the 'slog' of GCSEs

   b How does the original version of the sentence give this idea emphasis?
      Write ✎ two or three sentences explaining your ideas.

   ....

   ....

   ....

   ....

   ....

   ....

   ....

② How do I comment on the writer's use of sentence forms?

Writers often structure sentences to manipulate their impact and their emphasis.

① Look again at these four sentences from the first paragraph of the article.

A ┊ All over the country this month, GCSE pupils will be sitting down, once again, to slog through their exams. ┊

B ┊ Whether it's the chorus of sniffing, the three hours of cramping fingers, the coldly sweating armpits or the hotly anticipated questions that never appear, exams are an archetypal stress dream for a reason. ┊

C & D ┊ But I'm afraid they matter. They matter enormously. ┊

Using the suggestions below, write ✎ a sentence or two about each of sentences A–D, commenting on:

- the kind of **sentence structure** the writer has used
- the **impact** of the sentence structure
- how the sentence structure helps the writer to achieve their **intention**.

Sentence structure	Impact	Intention
A short sentence	which adds emphasis,	to describe the experience of facing GCSEs.
A longer sentence listing events or information	which highlights a key point or idea,	to advise anxious GCSE students.
A sentence which begins with a key word or phrase	which provides descriptive detail,	to reassure anxious GCSE students.
A sentence where key information is delayed to the end	which creates tension,	to entertain the reader.

Sentence A is ....

....

....

Sentence B is ....

....

....

Sentences C and D are ....

....

....

② Identify one further sentence in the article on page 26. Annotate ✎ your chosen sentence commenting on how it is structured, the impact of its structure and how it helps the writer to achieve their intention.

3 **How do I comment on sentence forms and other language choices?**

To effectively analyse a text, you need to link your comments on language and structure and focus them on the question you are answering.

1 Look again at the exam-style question you saw on page 25.

a Now look at the sentences below, written by a student in response to the exam-style question. Tick ✓ any that might help you answer the question because they:
- comment on the writer's use of language
- comment on the writer's use of sentence forms
- refer to key words in the exam-style question.

b Cross ✗ any that will not help you answer the question.

A.
Exams are not the time for peer pressure.

B.
cramping fingers... coldly sweating armpits

C.
Some of the strongest key points are delivered using very blunt, simple language.

D.
The writer uses lots of emotive language choices to describe the fear and anxiety of exams.

E.
The writer structures this point in a short sentence to add emphasis.

F.
The sentence structure effectively highlights the pressure that GCSE students are likely to experience.

G.
The writer suggests what you should and shouldn't do or think to help you cope with GCSEs.

H.
By referring to 'peer pressure' the writer is suggesting that you should do whatever works for you, regardless of what other people think.

2 Look again at the sentences above that you have ticked. Use 🖉 **some** or **all** of them to craft an effective paragraph of analysis in response to the question above. Aim to adapt and improve the sentences, linking them using adverbials or conjunctions like the ones below.

| however | for example | such as | in this way | although | because |

....

....

....

....

....

....

....

Commenting on sentence forms

To comment successfully on sentence forms, you need to:
- identify sentence forms selected for emphasis and/or impact
- analyse the impact of those sentence forms on the reader
- analyse how sentence forms and language choices work together to achieve that impact.

Now look at this exam-style question you saw at the start of the unit.

Exam-style question

You need to refer **only** to **Source 1** on how to survive the exam season.

How does the writer use language to make you, the reader, understand the experience of facing GCSE exams? **(12 marks)**

(1) Circle (A) the **key words in the question** that **either** tell you what you are being asked to do **or** you should include in every paragraph of your answer **or** both.

(2) Now look at two students' comments on this quotation from the source on page 26:

> A boy in a friend's science GCSE exam wore a pair of earplugs to muffle the maddening soundtrack of ticking clocks, sniffing classmates, squeaking chairs and sobbing companions.

Student A

By describing all these noises, the writer shows you what you can hear in an exam and how they are really 'maddening' when you are trying to take an exam, so it helps you understand the experience of facing GCSE exams.

Student B

The writer structures part of this sentence as a list of annoying noises, choosing vivid descriptive adjectives like 'ticking' and 'sniffing' and 'squeaking'. The list structure emphasises how many there are and how annoying they can be.

Which of the two students' comments is the most effective? Write (✏) a sentence or two explaining your choice. Use the bullet point list of key features at the top of the page to help you.

....

....

....

....

....

....

Your turn!

You are now going to write ✏ your own answer in response to the exam-style question focusing on the writer's use of sentence forms. Unit 3 focuses on how to analyse the writer's use of words, phrases and language features.

Exam-style question

You need to refer **only** to **Source 1** on how to survive the exam season.

How does the writer use language to make you, the reader, understand the experience of facing GCSE exams? **(12 marks)**

1 Note down ✏ **three** sentences whose structure helps the writer to make you, the reader, understand the experience of facing GCSE exams.

1.	2.	3.

2 For each of the sentences, note down ✏ some ideas you could include in your analysis of their structure and/or impact on the reader.

1.	2.	3.

3 For each of the sentences, note down ✏ how their impact helps the writer to convey the experience of facing GCSE exams.

1.	2.	3.

4 Use your ideas and planning from questions **1**–**3** to write ✏ your response to the exam-style question above on paper.

Review your skills

Check up

Review your response to the exam-style question on page 31. Tick ✓ the column to show how well you think you have done each of the following.

	Had a go ✓	Nearly there ✓	Got it! ✓
identified sentence forms crafted for effect	☐	☐	☐
commented on the impact of sentence forms	☐	☐	☐
commented on the impact of sentence forms and language choices	☐	☐	☐

Look over all of your work in this unit. Note down ✐ the three most important things to remember when you comment on sentence forms.

1. ....

2. ....

3. ....

Need more practice?

Here is another exam-style question, this time relating to Source C on page 75: another newspaper article called *A Back Seat Education*. You'll find some suggested points to refer to in the Answers section.

Exam-style question

You now need to refer **only** to **Source C**.

How does the writer use language to describe her experience of travelling on the school bus when she was a student?   (12 marks)

How confident do you feel about each of these **skills?** Colour ✐ in the bars.

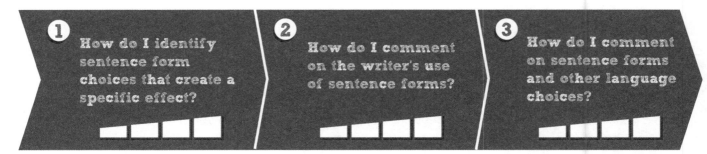

① How do I identify sentence form choices that create a specific effect?

② How do I comment on the writer's use of sentence forms?

③ How do I comment on sentence forms and other language choices?

Get started

Explain, comment on and analyse how writers use language and structure to achieve effects and influence readers (AO2)

⑤ Commenting on structure

This unit will help you comment on whole text structure. The skills you will build are to:

- identify ways in which a writer has structured a text
- explore the impact of the writer's structural choices
- develop your analysis of the writer's structural choices.

In the exam you will face questions like the one below. This is about the text on page 34. At the end of the unit you will write your own response to this question.

Exam-style question

This text is from the opening of a novel.

How has the writer structured the text to interest you as a reader?

You could write about:

- what the writer focuses your attention on at the beginning
- how and why the writer changes this focus as the extract develops
- any other structural features that interest you.

(8 marks)

The three key questions in the **skills boosts** will help you comment on language and structure.

① How do I identify significant whole text structure choices?

② How do I know why the writer has structured the text in this way?

③ How do I comment on whole text structure?

Read the extract on page 34 from the opening of a novel: *The Road Home* by Rose Tremain, published in 2008. You will tackle a 20th or 21st century fiction extract in the Reading section of your Paper 1 exam.

As you read, remember the following: ⊘

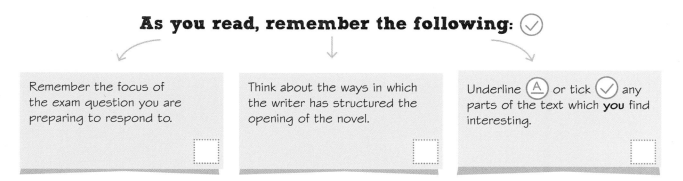

Remember the focus of the exam question you are preparing to respond to.

Think about the ways in which the writer has structured the opening of the novel.

Underline Ⓐ or tick ⊘ any parts of the text which **you** find interesting.

Lev is emigrating from Eastern Europe to live in Britain.

Source 1 The Road Home, Rose Tremain

On the coach, Lev chose a seat near the back and he sat huddled against the window, staring out at the land he was leaving: at the fields of sunflowers scorched by the dry wind, at the pig farms, at the quarries and rivers and at the wild garlic growing green at the edge of the road.

Lev wore a leather jacket and jeans and a leather cap pulled low over his eyes, and his handsome face was
5   gray-toned from his smoking, and in his hands he clutched an old red cotton handkerchief and a dented pack of Russian cigarettes. He would soon be forty-three. After some miles, as the sun came up, Lev took out a cigarette and stuck it between his lips, and the woman sitting next to him, a plump, contained person with moles like splashes of mud on her face, said quickly, "I'm sorry, but there is no smoking allowed on this bus." Lev knew this, had known it in advance, had tried to prepare himself mentally for the long agony of it. But even an unlit
10 cigarette was a companion — something to hold on to, something that had promise in it — and all he could be bothered to do now was to nod, just to show the woman that he'd heard what she'd said, reassure her that he wasn't going to cause trouble; because there they would have to sit for fifty hours or more, side by side, with their separate aches and dreams, like a married couple. They would hear each other's snores and sighs, smell the food and drink each had brought with them, note the degree to which each was fearful or unafraid, make short forays
15 into conversation. And then later, when they finally arrived in London, they would probably separate with barely a word or a look, walk out into a rainy morning, each alone and beginning a new life. And Lev thought how all of this was odd but necessary and already told him things about the world he was traveling to, a world in which he would break his back working — if only that work could be found. He would hold himself apart from other people, find corners and shadows in which to sit and smoke, demonstrate that he didn't need to belong, that his heart
20 remained in his own country.

There were two coach drivers. These men would take turns to drive and to sleep. There was an on-board lavatory, so the only stops the bus would make would be for gas. At gas stations, the passengers would be able to clamber off, walk a few paces, see wild flowers on a verge, soiled paper among bushes, sun or rain on the road. They might stretch up their arms, put on dark glasses against the onrush of nature's light, look for a clover leaf, smoke and
25 stare at the cars rushing by. Then they would be herded back onto the coach, resume their old attitudes, arm themselves for the next hundred miles, for the stink of another industrial zone or the sudden gleam of a lake, for rain and sunset and the approach of darkness on silent marshes. There would be times when the journey would seem to have no end.

1   How do I identify significant whole text structure choices?

To identify significant structural choices the writer has made in a text, you need to track the sequence in which the writer presents description or action, reveals character, and hints at the ways in which the story might develop.

1   In the source on page 34, underline Ⓐ and label 🖊 (A–G) where these key points appear in the text on page 34.

A. | Lev puts a cigarette in his mouth.   B. | Lev is leaving his home land.

C. | Lev imagines having to sit next to the woman on the long journey ahead.

D. | A woman tells him he is not allowed to smoke on the coach.

E. | Lev imagines the long journey ahead.   F. | Lev imagines his life in the United Kingdom.

G. | The writer describes Lev.

2   Now think about what the writer has revealed about her characters and their dialogue, and the events, settings and mood in each of the sections you identified in question ①. Use your answers to the questions below to annotate 🖊 the text on page 34. Tick ✓ each question as you answer it.

- **Characters**

  ☐ What impression does the writer create of Lev?

- **Dialogue**:

  ☐ What does the conversation about the cigarette suggest?

- **Events**:

  ☐ What impression do Lev's thoughts about the journey ahead create?

- **Settings**:

  ☐ What impression does the writer create of Lev's homeland?

  ☐ What impression does the writer create of the life he expects to lead in the UK?

- **Mood**:

  ☐ What kind of mood does the writer create in the extract?

3   Can you identify any patterns, similarities, contrasts or other connections between any of the key points you identified in question ① **and/or** any of the impressions you noted in question ②?

Write 🖊 a sentence or two below, summarising them.

....

....

....

....

....

2 How do I know why the writer has structured the text in this way?

To explore a text's structure, you need to think about:

- the writer's **intention**

- how the ideas, description, dialogue or other features in the text are selected and ordered to achieve that intention.

> **intention:** the impact the writer intends the text to have on the reader

(1) Look again at the exam-style question which you are focusing on in this unit.

Exam-style question

How has the writer structured the text to <u>interest you as a reader</u>?

Tick ✓ any of the writer's **intentions** listed below which you think the writer of the text on page 34 has achieved in order to **interest readers**. Use the spaces to add your own ideas.

To interest readers in the opening of a novel, it might be the writer's intention:

A. to introduce or develop characters whose story the reader will want to follow.

B. to create situations or problems which will develop as the story develops.

C. to suggest there is a mystery to be solved.

D. to shock, surprise and/or intrigue the reader.

E. to prompt the reader to ask questions.

F. ....

G. ....

(2) Which of the **intentions** you ticked in question (1) has the writer achieved through the **features** listed below? Circle (A) the relevant letters.

The writer creates **characters**:	A	B	C	D	E	F	G
The writer uses **dialogue**:	A	B	C	D	E	F	G
The writer describes **events**:	A	B	C	D	E	F	G
The writer describes **settings**:	A	B	C	D	E	F	G
The writer establishes the **mood**:	A	B	C	D	E	F	G

(3) Note down ✏ **up to three** questions that the extract on page 34 prompted you to ask or that you suspect the writer will answer as the story develops.

....

....

....

....

3 How do I comment on whole text structure?

When you analyse the structure of a fiction text, you should aim to comment on how the writer has structured the extract **and** the impact of the writer's choices **at this point in the story**. For example, when writing about the opening of a novel, you should comment on:

- how the writer has structured the text
- why the writer has done this at the start of the novel.

1. Look at some students' comments about the opening of the novel *The Road Home*.

A.
> In this short extract, the writer gives the reader a really clear picture of Lev's journey from his old life to his new life. This makes the reader want to find out more about this character and what happens to him.

B.
> At the very beginning of the extract, the writer describes the 'fields of sunflowers' and the 'wild garlic' of Lev's own country.

C.
> The writer describes where Lev has come from, how he imagines his new life will be, and how horrible his long, long coach journey is.

D.
> The writer describes the 'fifty hours' of the coach journey and the sounds and smells of the other passengers.

E.
> The writer engages and interests the reader by making us feel sympathy for Lev.

F.
> The writer contrasts the life that Lev is leaving and the new life he is going to begin in London.

G.
> The reader wants to find out what happens when Lev arrives in London. The writer has Lev imagining this to make the reader want to find out if it turns out the way he imagined it.

H.
> The writer shows us the beginning and end of the journey encouraging the reader to compare and contrast them.

a. Which of these comments, if any, would you **not** include in an analysis of the ways in which the writer has structured the text to interest readers? Cross ⊗ them.

b. Tick ✓ the three comments which you feel give the **most effective analysis** of the ways in which the writer has structured the text to interest readers.

c. Write ✐ a sentence or two, summarising what you feel makes a successful comment on the structure of a fiction extract.

....

....

....

....

....

Commenting on language and structure

To write an effective analysis of the writer's use of whole text structure, you need to explore:

- the selection and structure of ideas in the whole text
- how those ideas contribute to the text as a whole, for example as the opening of a novel
- the impact of the whole text's structure and features on the reader.

Look at this exam-style question.

Exam-style question

This text is from the opening of a novel.

How has the writer structured the text to interest you as a reader?

You could write about:

- what the writer focuses your attention on at the beginning
- how and why the writer changes this focus as the extract develops
- any other structural features that interest you.

(8 marks)

Look at this paragraph written by one student in response to the exam-style question above.

effective choice of quotation and reference to the text

The writer begins the novel with a journey so it feels like the reader will be making the journey with him from his own country to the UK by coach. There is a big difference between his life in his own country and the new life he imagines. The writer describes 'fields of sunflowers' and 'pig farms' but does not really describe how he imagines London so the reader can expect the shock he will have when he arrives in Britain and will want to find out what happens and how he deals with it. This is the main way the writer interests the reader, by getting us to take a journey into the unknown with Lev.

analyses the impact of the extract as the opening of a novel

identifies the writer's intention

focuses the analysis on the question

analyses the impact of the writer's use of structure

Can you identify all the different things the student has included in this paragraph?

Link ✎ the annotations to the paragraph to show where the student has included them.

Your turn!

You are now going to write your own answer in response to the exam-style question.

Exam-style question

This text is from the opening of a novel.

How has the writer structured the text to interest you as a reader?

You could write about:

• what the writer focuses your attention on at the beginning

• how and why the writer changes this focus as the extract develops

• any other structural features that interest you. (8 marks)

You should spend around 10–15 minutes on this type of question, so should aim to write two or three paragraphs ✏.

(**1**) Use the table below to plan **three paragraphs**:

	How the writer has structured the extract	The impact this has on the reader	How this interests the reader in the text
1			
2			
3			

Now use your planning to write ✏ a response to the exam-style question above on paper.

Review your skills

Check up

Review your response to the exam-style question on page 39. Tick ✓ the column to show how well you think you have done each of the following.

	Had a go ✓	Nearly there ✓	Got it! ✓
identified the writer's structural choices	☐	☐	☐
explored the impact of the writer's structural choices	☐	☐	☐
commented on the impact of the writer's structural choices	☐	☐	☐

Look over all of your work in this unit.

Note down ✐ the three things you find most challenging about analysing a writer's use of structure. Rank them from 1 (the most challenging) to 3 (the least challenging).

1. .... ☐

2. .... ☐

3. .... ☐

Need more practice? •••

Here is another exam-style question, this time relating to Source A on page 73, an extract from *The Birds* by Daphne Du Maurier. You'll find some suggested points to refer to in the Answers section.

Exam-style question

This text is from near the beginning of a short story.

How has the writer structured the text to interest you as a reader?

You could write about:
- what the writer focuses your attention on at the beginning
- how and why the writer changes this focus as the extract develops
- any other structural features that interest you.

(8 marks)

How confident do you feel about each of these **skills?** Colour ✐ in the bars.

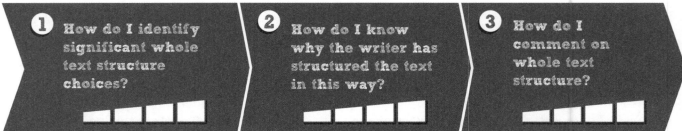

1. How do I identify significant whole text structure choices?

2. How do I know why the writer has structured the text in this way?

3. How do I comment on whole text structure?

⑥ Evaluating a text

This unit will help you evaluate a text. The skills you will build are to:

- recognise the writer's intentions
- identify where in the text the writer has attempted to achieve that intention
- develop your analysis of the writer's choices and their impact on you as a reader
- develop your evaluation of how successfully the writer has achieved their intention and its impact on you as a reader.

In the exam you will face questions like the one below. This is about the text on page 42. This unit will prepare you to write your own response to this question.

Exam-style question

Focus this part of your answer on the second half of the source, **from line 16 to the end**.

A student, having read this section of the text said: "The writer shows Ugwu's different feelings about his new life and his new job. You feel anxious but excited for him."

To what extent do you agree?

In your response, you could:

- consider your own impressions of Ugwu's different feelings
- evaluate how the writer has created these impressions
- support your opinions with quotations from the text.

(20 marks)

The three key questions in the **skills boosts** will help you prepare your response.

① How do I identify which parts of the text to write about?

② How do I analyse the writer's choices?

③ How do I evaluate the writer's choices?

Read the extract on page 42 from *Half of a Yellow Sun* by Chimamanda Ngozi Adichie. You will tackle a 20th or 21st century fiction extract in the Reading section of your Paper 1 exam.

As you read, remember the following: ⊘

If you lose understanding of the text, stop and reread from the last sentence or paragraph that you clearly understood.

Mark or highlight any parts of the text relevant to the question you are going to answer: where the writer shows or suggests Ugwu's feelings.

It is the late 1960s in Nigeria. Ugwu, a thirteen year old boy from a poor village, is going to work for a Professor of Mathematics as his houseboy, or personal servant.

Source 1 Half of a Yellow Sun, Chimamanda Ngozi Adichie

Master was a little crazy; he had spent too many years reading books overseas, talked to himself in his office, did not always return greetings, and had too much hair. Ugwu's aunty said this in a low voice as they walked on the path. "But he is a good man," she added. "And as long as you work well, you will eat well. You will even eat meat every day." She stopped to spit; the saliva left her mouth with a sucking sound and landed on the grass.

5 Ugwu did not believe that anybody, not even this master he was going to live with, ate meat *every day*. He did not disagree with his aunty, though, because he was too choked with expectation, too busy imagining his new life away from the village. They had been walking for a while now, since they got off the lorry at the motor park, and the afternoon sun burned the back of his neck. But he did not mind. He was prepared to walk hours more in even hotter sun. He had never seen anything like the streets that appeared after they went past the university gates,

10 streets so smooth and tarred that he itched to lay his cheek down on them. He would never be able to describe to his sister Anulika how the bungalows here were painted the color of the sky and sat side by side like polite well-dressed men, how the hedges separating them were trimmed so flat on top that they looked like tables wrapped with leaves.

His aunty walked faster, her slippers making *slap-slap* sounds that echoed in the silent street. Ugwu wondered
15 if she, too, could feel the coal tar getting hotter underneath, through her thin soles. They went past a sign, ODIM STREET, and Ugwu mouthed *street*, as he did whenever he saw an English word that was not too long. He smelled something sweet, heady, as they walked into a **compound**, and was sure it came from the white flowers clustered on the bushes at the entrance. The bushes were shaped like slender hills. The lawn glistened. Butterflies hovered above.

20 "I told Master you will learn everything fast, **osiso-osiso**," his aunty said. Ugwu nodded attentively although she had already told him this many times, as often as she told him the story of how his good fortune came about: while she was sweeping the corridor in the mathematics department a week ago, she heard Master say that he needed a houseboy to do his cleaning, and she immediately said she could help, speaking before his typist or office messenger could offer to bring someone.

25 "I will learn fast, Aunty," Ugwu said. He was staring at the car in the garage; a strip of metal ran around its blue body like a necklace.

"Remember, what you will answer whenever he calls you is *Yes, sah!*"

"Yes, sah!" Ugwu repeated.

They were standing before the glass door. Ugwu held back from reaching out to touch the cement wall, to see how
30 different it would feel from the mud walls of his mother's hut that still bore the faint patterns of moulding fingers. For a brief moment, he wished he were back there now, in his mother's hut, under the dim coolness of the thatch roof; or in his aunty's hut, the only one in the village with a corrugated iron roof.

His aunty tapped on the glass. Ugwu could see the white curtains behind the door. A voice said, in English, "Yes? Come in."

compound: the university buildings where Ugwu will work in his new job
osiso-osiso: a word in Igbo, the language spoken by Ugwu and his aunty, meaning 'very fast'

How do I identify which parts of the text to write about?

In every written text, the writer has an **intention**. In order to evaluate a text effectively, you need to decide what you think the **writer's intention** is, and **where in the text the writer has achieved it**.

> **intention:** the impact the writer wants the text to have on the reader

(1) Here is one student's ideas about the writer's intention in the text on page 42.

> The writer shows Ugwu's different feelings about his new life and his new job. You feel anxious but excited for him.

   a Do you agree? ✓   Yes, completely ☐   No, not at all ☐   I partly agree ☐

   b Why? ✏ ....

....

(2) Look carefully through the extract again, from line 16 to the end. Highlight or underline Ⓐ any sections of the text in which the writer clearly states Ugwu's feelings about his new life and job. Annotate ✏ the highlighted text, noting Ugwu's feelings at that point in the extract.

(3) Now look closely at all the different elements below that the writer has included in the extract from line 16 to the end. Tick ✓ any that the writer uses to suggest or hint at Ugwu's feelings about his new life and job:

☐   Ugwu wonders if his aunty can feel the hot street through her shoes

☐   Ugwu smells sweet flowers in the university compound

☐   Ugwu agrees he will learn his new duties quickly

☐   The narrator describes Ugwu's good fortune in being offered his new job

☐   Ugwu stares at the car in the garage

☐   Ugwu will always answer 'Yes, sah!'

☐   Ugwu stops himself touching the cement wall

☐   Ugwu wishes he was back in his village

(4) Look at the list of emotions below.

ambition	anger	disappointment	discomfort	excitement

happiness	envy	pressure	sadness	uncertainty

   a Circle Ⓐ the feelings that the writer suggests Ugwu might be feeling in the extract from lines 16 to the end.

   b Which of the elements that you ticked in question **3** suggest the feelings you have identified? Annotate ✏ the elements you have circled with the emotions. Some elements may suggest two or more different feelings.

2 How do I analyse the writer's choices?

Your evaluation should **analyse how** the writer's choices of language and structure contribute to the writer's intention **and** the impact that these choices have on the reader.

① Effective analytical comments explore the writer's choices and their impact on the reader.

Look at this quotation. 'I told Master you will learn everything fast, *osiso-osiso*,' his aunty said. Ugwu nodded attentively

a What impact does the writer intend these sentences to have on the reader?

Circle Ⓐ any of the suggestions below and/or add your own ideas.

anxiety	excitement	impatience	sympathy

annoyance	admiration		

b How do the writer's choices contribute to that impact? Note 🖉 your ideas below.

i. The choice of verb form: You will learn

ii. The choice of adjectives fast and osiso-osiso .

iii. The adverb attentively to describe Ugwu's response.

② Use the notes you made above to write 🖉 two or three sentences analysing how the writer's choices in this quotation reveal Ugwu's feelings and the impact these choices have on the reader.

....

....

....

....

....

③ Underline Ⓐ another quotation in the extract which you feel reveals Ugwu's feelings. Write 🖉 two or three sentences, analysing how its language and structure contribute to the writer's intention and its impact on the reader.

....

....

....

....

....

How do I evaluate the writer's choices?

An effective evaluation should explore **how** the writer has achieved their intention, its impact on the reader **and how effectively** the writer has achieved this.

1 In each of the quotations you choose and the comments you make in your evaluation, you need to think about how successfully the writer of the text achieves their intention.

a Choose and circle Ⓐ **one** of the quotations below which you feel:

- contributes to the writer's intention of describing Ugwu's feelings
- has a significant impact on the reader
- will allow you to comment on the writer's choices of language and/or sentence forms.

> "I will learn fast, Aunty," Ugwu said.

> Remember, what you will answer whenever he calls you is *Yes, sah*! "Yes, sah!" Ugwu repeated.

> Ugwu held back from reaching out to touch the cement wall

b Focusing on your chosen quotation, underline Ⓐ any of the writer's choices of language and/or sentence forms which you think are significant.

2 Use these key questions and phrases to help you write 🖉 about the quotation you chose above.

What does the writer do?		How successfully?	What impact does this have on the reader?		
The writer	suggests	effectively			feels...
The author	implies	successfully			recognises...
The text	describes	clearly	The reader		believes...
The extract	emphasises	powerfully			is encouraged to...

For example:

> *The writer effectively suggests the idea that Ugwu feels impressed by the city he has come to live in: 'He was staring at the car in the garage; a strip of metal ran around its blue body like a necklace.' The writer uses the verb 'staring' to imply that the car has captured Ugwu's attention and the simile of 'a necklace' to suggest that he thinks the car is beautiful and valuable. In this way, the reader is encouraged to see how different Ugwu's new life will be compared to his old life.*

Now write 🖉 your own response to your chosen quotation.

....

....

....

....

....

How do I evaluate a text?

To successfully evaluate a text, you need to:

- recognise the writer's intention which is suggested in the exam question you are answering
- identify where in the text the writer has attempted to achieve their intention(s)
- select quotations from the text which support your ideas and allow you to comment on the writer's choices
- explore the writer's choices closely, focusing on **how** the writer has achieved their intention, its impact on the reader, and **how successfully** the writer has achieved this.

Look at this exam-style question.

Exam-style question

Focus this part of your answer on the second half of the source, **from line 16 to the end.**

A student, having read this section of the text said: "The writer shows Ugwu's different feelings about his new life and his new job. You feel anxious but excited for him."

To what extent do you agree?

In your response, you could:

- consider your own impressions of Ugwu's different feelings
- evaluate how the writer has created these impressions
- support your opinions with quotations from the text.

(20 marks)

Then look at a paragraph from one student's response to it.

uses key words from the question

evidence from the text

comments on vocabulary and/ or sentence form choices

comments on how this helps to achieve the writer's intention

comments on the impact of the text on the reader

uses evaluative language to comment on the writer's success in achieving her intention

The writer suggests the feeling of pressure which Ugwu must have as he starts his new job. His aunty tells him 'often ...how his good fortune came about'. The phrase 'good fortune' suggests how lucky Ugwu is to have got this job and the adverb 'often' emphasises that Ugwu's aunty wants him to appreciate how lucky he has been. The writer does not say that Ugwu feels upset or annoyed by this pressure which suggests to me that he accepts it and understands what is expected of him. In this way the writer effectively suggests the pressure and Ugwu's feelings about it.

Can you identify all the different things the student has included in this paragraph?

Link (✏) the annotations to the paragraph to show where the student has included them.

Your turn!

You are now going to write your own answer in response to the exam-style question.

Exam-style question

Focus this part of your answer on the second half of the source, **from line 16 to the end**.

A student, having read this section of the text said: "The writer shows Ugwu's different feelings about his new life and his new job. You feel anxious but excited for him."

To what extent do you agree?

In your response, you could:

- consider your own impressions of Ugwu's different feelings
- evaluate how the writer has created these impressions
- support your opinions with quotations from the text. **(20 marks)**

Before you write your response, complete the tasks below to help you prepare.

1. Think about how you might begin your answer to the question. You could focus on the feeling which is most strongly suggested in the extract. (✐)

2. You should spend around 20–25 minutes on this question, so should aim to write three or four further paragraphs. The first paragraph will be the introduction you planned in question (1) above. Note down (✐) the different elements of the extract on which you will focus in the remaining paragraphs.

3. Select the quotations that you will explore in each paragraph. You could underline (Ⓐ) them on the extract on page 42 and add the line number of each quotation to your notes above.

4. Think about the comments you will make on the writer's choices in each paragraph. Annotate (✐) the quotations you have selected on the extract, identifying key vocabulary and sentence form choices which help the writer to show Ugwu's different feelings.

5. Now write (✐) your response to the exam-style question above on paper.

Review your skills

Check up

Review your response to the exam-style question on page 47. Tick ✓ the column to show how well you think you have done each of the following.

	Not quite ✓	Nearly there ✓	Got it! ✓
identified elements of the text which show Ugwu's different feelings	☐	☐	☐
identified relevant quotations	☐	☐	☐
commented in detail on the writer's choices	☐	☐	☐
commented in detail on the impact of the writer's choices on the reader	☐	☐	☐
evaluated the writer's success	☐	☐	☐

Need more practice?

Here is another exam-style question, this time relating to Source A on page 73: an extract from *The Birds* by Daphne Du Maurier. You'll find some suggested points to refer to in the Answers section.

Exam-style question

Focus this part of your answer on the second half of the source, **from line 22 to the end**.

A student, having read this section of the text said: "The writer makes this attack really shocking and frightening. It makes me want to find out why the birds are attacking and what will happen next."

To what extent do you agree?

In your response, you could:
- consider your own impressions of the attack and of the family's reactions
- evaluate how the writer creates a shocking and frightening atmosphere
- support your opinions with quotations from the text. (20 marks)

How confident do you feel about each of these **skills**? Colour 🖉 in the bars.

1 How do I identify which parts of the text to write about?

2 How do I analyse the writer's choices?

3 How do I evaluate the writer's choices?

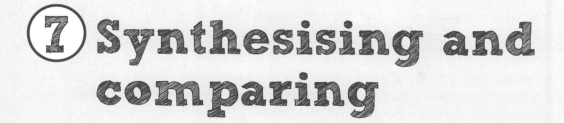
(7) Synthesising and comparing

This unit will help you synthesise information and ideas from two texts and compare them. The skills you will build are to:

- identify **explicit** differences and similarities in two texts
- identify differences and similarities that are **implied** in two texts
- synthesise and compare the differences or similarities in two texts.

In the exam you will face questions like the one below. This is about the texts on page 50. At the end of the unit you will write your own response to this question.

Exam-style question

You need to refer to **source A** and **source B** for this question.

Use details from **both** sources. Write a summary of the differences between the family relationships.

(8 marks)

The three key questions in the **skills boosts** will help you synthesise and compare similarities or differences in two texts.

1. How do I begin to identify similarities or differences?

2. How do I compare implied ideas?

3. How do I synthesise similarities or differences and compare them?

Read the extracts on page 50 from Clive James' autobiography *Unreliable Memoirs* published in 1980, and from Charles Dickens' *Sketches by Boz*, published in 1836. You will tackle one 20th or 21st century non-fiction extract and one 19th century non-fiction extract in the Reading section of your Paper 2 exam.

As you read, remember the following: ⊘

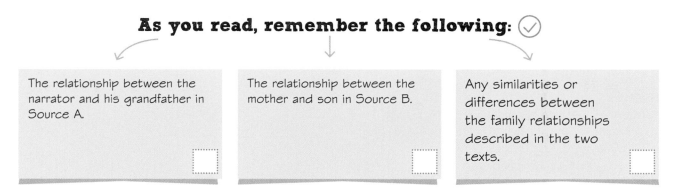

The relationship between the narrator and his grandfather in Source A.

The relationship between the mother and son in Source B.

Any similarities or differences between the family relationships described in the two texts.

The writer remembers his grandfather, whom he lived with when he was very young.

Source A Unreliable Memoirs, Clive James

I remember him as a tall, barely articulate source of smells. The principal smells were of mouldy cloth, mothballs, seaweed, powerful tobacco and the tars that collect in the stem of a very old pipe. When he was smoking he was invisible. When he wasn't smoking he was merely hard to pick out in the gloom. You could track him down by listening for his constant, low-pitched, incoherent mumble. From his carpet slippers to his moustache was twice
5   as high as I could reach. The moustache was **saffron** with nicotine. Everywhere else he was either grey or tortoise-shell mottle. His teeth were both.

I remember he bared them at me one Christmas dinner. It was because he was choking on a coin in a mouthful of plum pudding. It was the usual Australian Christmas dinner, taking place in the middle of the day. Despite the temperature being 100 °F in the shade, there had been the full panoply of ragingly hot food, topped off
10   with a volcanic plum pudding smothered in scalding custard. My mother had naturally spiced the pudding with **sixpences and threepenny bits**, called zacs and trays respectively. Grandpa had collected one of these in the oesophagus. He gave a protracted, strangled gurgle which for a long time we all took to be the beginning of some anecdote. Then Aunt Dot bounded out of her chair and hit him in the back. By some miracle she did not snap his calcified spine. Coated with black crumbs and custard, the zac streaked out of his mouth like a **dum-dum** and
15   ricocheted off a tureen.

Dickens describes a mother and son he saw when walking through London.

Source B Sketches by Boz, Charles Dickens

We were walking leisurely down the **Old Bailey** and saw two persons descending the steps. We could not help stopping and observing them.

They were an elderly woman, of decent appearance, though evidently poor, and a boy of about fourteen or fifteen. The woman was crying bitterly; she carried a small bundle in her hand, and the boy followed at a short distance
5   behind her. Their little history was obvious. The boy was her son, to whose early comfort she had perhaps sacrificed her own--for whose sake she had borne misery without repining, and poverty without a murmur--looking steadily forward to the time, when he who had so long witnessed her struggles for himself, might be enabled to make some exertions for their joint support. He had **formed dissolute connexions**; idleness had led to crime; and he had been committed to take his trial for some petty theft. He had been long in prison, and,
10   after receiving some trifling additional punishment, had been ordered to be discharged that morning. It was his first offence, and his poor old mother, still hoping to reclaim him, had been waiting at the gate to implore him to return home.

We cannot forget the boy; he descended the steps with a dogged look, shaking his head with an air of bravado and obstinate determination. They walked a few paces, and paused. The woman put her hand upon his shoulder
15   in an agony of entreaty, and the boy sullenly raised his head as if in refusal. It was a brilliant morning, and every object looked fresh and happy in the broad, gay sunlight; he gazed round him for a few moments, bewildered with the brightness of the scene, for it was long since he had beheld anything save the gloomy walls of a prison. Perhaps the wretchedness of his mother made some impression on the boy's heart; perhaps some undefined recollection of the time when he was a happy child, and she his only friend, and best companion, crowded on him–
20   he burst into tears; and covering his face with one hand, and hurriedly placing the other in his mother's, walked away with her.

saffron: yellow
sixpences and threepenny bits: coins
dum-dum: a type of bullet
Old Bailey: The road in which the Old Bailey, the Central Criminal Court of London, is situated
formed dissolute connexions: fallen in with the wrong crowd

1   How do I begin to identify similarities or differences?

Identifying **explicit** ideas and information in the two texts is the first stage in beginning to compare them.

> explicit: clearly stated

(1) Look at one student's notes, summarising all of the information and detail explicitly stated in the two texts on page 50.

Draw ✏ lines linking any detail from Source A to any detail from Source B which shows a similarity between the two texts. Label ✏ these lines with the letter 'S'. Now draw ✏ lines linking any detail from Source A to any detail from Source B which shows a different between the two texts. Label ✏ these lines with the letter 'D'.

Source A: Unreliable Memoirs	Source B: Sketches by Boz
The narrator is writing about when he was a child.	The writer watches a poor woman and her son come out of the Old Bailey.
The text is about the narrator's elderly grandfather.	The woman is crying.
His grandfather makes a lot of smells.	The boy has just come out of prison for theft.
His grandfather smokes heavily.	The boy's mother has come to persuade the boy to come home with her.
His grandfather mumbles and is difficult to understand.	At first the boy refuses to go with her.
His grandfather has discoloured teeth.	The boy begins to cry.
His grandfather choked on a coin one Christmas.	The boy walks away with his mother.

(2) Write ✏ a sentence or two, summarising the similarities and differences in the two extracts.

....

....

....

....

2 How do I compare implied ideas?

Once you have identified any **explicit** similarities or differences in the texts, you need to focus on what you can **infer** from the texts which will help you to answer the question.

(1) Look closely at the quotations below, taken from the source texts on page 50.

Tick ✓ any of the quotations from which you can infer information or ideas about the family relationship described in the extracts and annotate ✐ them with your ideas.

Source A: Unreliable Memoirs	Source B: Sketches by Boz
A. I remember him as a tall, barely articulate source of smells. ☐	A. The woman was crying bitterly… the boy followed at a short distance behind her. ☐
B. You could track him down by listening for his constant, low-pitched, incoherent mumble. ☐	B. The boy was her son, to whose early comfort she had perhaps sacrificed her own. ☐
C. He gave a protracted, strangled gurgle which for a long time we all took to be the beginning of some anecdote. ☐	C. The woman put her hand upon his shoulder in an agony of entreaty, and the boy sullenly raised his head as if in refusal. ☐
D. By some miracle she did not snap his calcified spine. ☐	D. Perhaps the wretchedness of his mother made some impression on the boy's heart ☐
E. Coated with black crumbs and custard, the zac streaked out of his mouth like a **dum-dum** and ricocheted off a tureen. ☐	E. covering his face with one hand, and hurriedly placing the other in his mother's, walked away with her. ☐

(2) In what ways are the family relationships described in the two texts similar or different?

a Circle Ⓐ **one** of the boxed words in each of the sentences below to sum up the similarities or differences in the family relationships described in the two texts.

				Source A quote	Source B quote
Both	Neither	One	of the relationships seem(s) very affectionate.		
Both	Neither	One	of the relationships is/are very strong.		
Both	Neither	One	of the relationships show(s) some unkindness.		
Both	Neither	One	of the relationships change(s) in the extract.		

b Choose a quote from **each** of the texts above as evidence to support your answers. Write ✐ the letter of your chosen quotations at the end of each sentence.

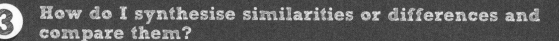

Skills boost

3 How do I synthesise similarities or differences and compare them?

To effectively synthesise and compare information and ideas from two texts, you must make sure you are selecting information which is relevant to the question you are answering.

(1) Look again at the exam-style question you saw at the start of this unit.

Exam-style question

Use details from **both** sources. Write a summary of the differences between the family relationships.

Which of these points are relevant to the question above? Tick ✓ them.

A. In Source A the writer suggests that none of his family can understand the grandfather so their relationship with him seems strange and distant. ☐

B. In Source B the writer describes an emotional reunion between the mother and her son which suggests a very strong bond between them. ☐

C. The narrator of Source A presents his grandfather's physical appearance in some detail. ☐

D. The narrator of Source B does not describe the mother and son in much detail but says they are 'evidently poor'. ☐

E. Source A focuses on the problems that his grandfather's old age caused, mainly for the rest of the family. ☐

F. Source B focuses on the problems that young people can cause their families. ☐

(2) Look again at the points you ticked above. Use them to write ✎ sentences about the similarities shared by the narrators of the two texts.

You can **link** comments on the similarities and differences in texts using words and phrases such as:

| Similarly... | In the same way... | However... | On the other hand... | ...whereas... | ...but... |

or **synthesise** the similarities in two texts using words such as: | Both... | Neither... | Each... |

....
....
....
....
....
....
....

Synthesising and comparing

To compare two texts, synthesising key information effectively, you need to:

- identify relevant information and ideas which are explicitly stated in the texts
- identify relevant information and ideas which are implied in the texts
- synthesise the relevant information and ideas from the texts to make relevant and valid comparisons.

Look at this exam-style question.

Exam-style question

You need to refer to **source A** and **source B** for this question.

Use details from **both** sources. Write a summary of the differences between the family relationships.

(8 marks)

(1) Now look at a paragraph from one student's response to the exam-style question above.

> Both of the texts show difficult family relationships, however they are very different. In Source B the woman and her son overcome their problems and the boy seems more like a child by the end of the extract as he cries and holds his mother's hand. In Source A, however, the narrator is cruel about his grandpa all the way through the extract which makes me think he is using the story to make the reader laugh.

(a) Here are the key features of an effective answer. Cross ⊗ the key features of an effective answer that this student **has not** achieved in this paragraph and tick ⊘ the key features of an effective answer that this student **has** achieved.

A. Focuses comments closely on the question.

B. Links or synthesises the different comments on the two texts.

C. Uses a relevant quotation or textual reference as evidence from each text.

(b) Annotate ✎ the paragraph to show which parts of the paragraph achieve which key feature.

Your turn!

You are now going to write your own answer in response to the exam-style question.

Exam-style question

You need to refer to **source A** and **source B** for this question.

Use details from **both** sources. Write a summary of the differences between the family relationships.

(8 marks)

1. You should spend 10–15 minutes on this kind of question, so should aim to write ✏ two or three paragraphs. Use the space below to plan three paragraphs.

	Differences	Source A: Evidence	Source B: Evidence
1			
2			
3			

2. Now write ✏ your response to the exam-style question above on paper.

Review your skills

Check up

Review your response to the exam-style question on page 55. Tick ⊘ the column to show how well you think you have done each of the following.

	Had a go ⊘	Nearly there ⊘	Got it! ⊘
identified **explicit** differences and similarities in two texts	☐	☐	☐
identified differences and similarities that are **implied** in two texts	☐	☐	☐
synthesised and compared the differences or similarities in two texts	☐	☐	☐

Need more practice?

Here is another exam-style question, this time relating to Source B on page 74 , an extract from *The Private Diary of the Master of a London Ragged School*, published in 1850, a and Source C on page 75, *A Back Seat Education*, a newspaper article published in 2016. You'll find some suggested points to refer to in the Answers section.

Exam-style question

You need to refer to **source B** and **source C** for this question:

Write a summary of the different situations the young people are in. Use details from **both** sources.

(8 marks)

Use evidence from both texts to support your answer.

How confident do you feel about each of these **skills?** Colour ⊘ in the bars.

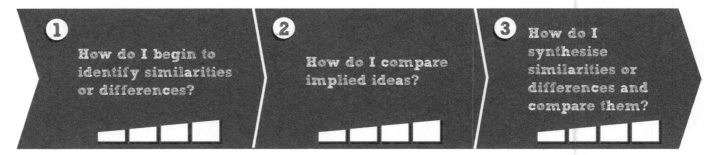

① How do I begin to identify similarities or differences?

② How do I compare implied ideas?

③ How do I synthesise similarities or differences and compare them?

Compare writers' ideas and perspectives, as well as how these are conveyed (AO3)

⑧ Comparing ideas and attitudes

This unit will help you learn how to compare the writers' ideas and attitudes in two texts. The skills you will build are to:

- identify the writer's ideas and attitudes
- identify similarities and differences in the ideas and attitudes in two texts
- develop a comparison of the ways in which the writers convey their ideas and attitudes
- structure a comparison of the writer's ideas and attitudes in two texts.

In the exam you will face questions like the one below. This is about the texts on page 58. At the end of the unit you will write your own response to this question.

Exam-style question

For this question, you need to refer to the **whole of source A** together with the **whole of source B**.

Compare how the writers have conveyed their different views and experiences of the places they describe.

In your answer, you could:
- compare their different views and experiences
- compare the methods they use to convey those views and experiences
- support your ideas with quotations from both texts. (16 marks)

Before you tackle the question you will work through three key questions in the **skills boosts** to help you compare the writer's ideas and attitudes.

① How do I identify and compare relevant ideas and attitudes?

② How do I develop my comparison of ideas and attitudes?

③ How do I structure my comparison?

Read the extracts on page 58 from *Eothen* by Alexander Kinglake, written in 1844, and *The Lost Continent* by Bill Bryson, published in 1989. You will tackle two non-fiction extracts, one from the 19th century and one from the 20th or 21st century, in the Reading section of your Paper 2 exam.

As you read, remember the following: ⊘

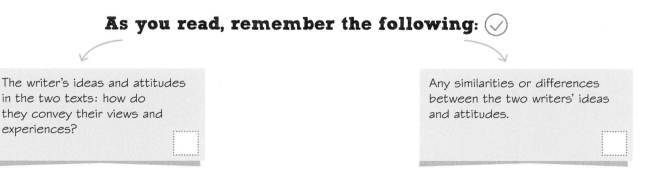

The writer's ideas and attitudes in the two texts: how do they convey their views and experiences?

Any similarities or differences between the two writers' ideas and attitudes.

In 1844, Alexander Kinglake wrote an account of his travels through Egypt.

Source A Eothen, Alexander Kinglake

I went to see and to explore the Pyramids.

Familiar to one from the days of early childhood are the forms of the Egyptian Pyramids, and now, as I approached them from the banks of the Nile, I had no print, no picture before me, and yet the old shapes were there; there was no change; they were just as I had always known them. Yet it was not till I came to the base of the great
5　Pyramid that reality began to weigh upon my mind. Strange to say, the bigness of the distinct blocks of stones was the first sign by which I attained to feel the immensity of the whole pile. When I came, and trod, and touched with my hands, and climbed, in order that by climbing I might come to the top of one single stone, then, and almost suddenly, a cold sense and understanding of the Pyramid's enormity came down, overcasting my brain.

When I was very young I was often in time of night the victim of a strange kind of mental oppression. I lay in my
10　bed perfectly conscious, and with open eyes, but without power to speak or to move, and all the while my brain was oppressed to distraction by the presence of a single and abstract idea of solid immensity. Well, now my eyes saw and knew, and my hands and my feet informed my understanding that there was nothing at all abstract about the great Pyramid — it was a big triangle, sufficiently **concrete**, easy to see, and rough to the touch; it could not, of course, affect me with the peculiar sensation which I have been talking of, but yet there was something akin to that old nightmare agony in the terrible completeness with which a mere mass of masonry could fill and load my mind.

The writer describes a visit to the Grand Canyon in the USA.

Source B The Lost Continent, Bill Bryson

Nothing prepares you for the Grand Canyon. Your mind, unable to deal with anything on this scale, just shuts down and for many long moments you are a human vacuum, without speech or breath, but just a deep, inexpressible awe that anything on this earth could be so vast, so beautiful, so silent. Even children are stilled by it. I was a particularly talkative and obnoxious child, but it stopped me cold. I can remember rounding a corner
5　and standing there agog while a mouthful of half-formed jabber just rolled backwards down my throat, forever unuttered.

The scale of the Grand Canyon is almost beyond comprehension. It is ten miles across, a mile deep, 180 miles long. You could set the Empire State Building down in it and still be thousands of feet above it. Indeed you could set the whole of Manhattan down inside it and you would still be so high above it that buses would be like ants
10　and people would be invisible, and not a sound would reach you. The thing that gets you - that gets everyone - is the silence. The Grand Canyon just swallows sound. The sense of space and emptiness is overwhelming. Nothing happens out there. Down below you on the canyon floor, far, far away, is the thing that carved it: the Colorado River. It is 300 feet wide, but from the canyon's lip it looks thin and insignificant. It looks like an old shoelace. Everything is dwarfed by this mighty hole.

concrete: solid, real, as in 'concrete evidence'

① How do I identify and compare relevant ideas and attitudes?

Before you can develop your comparison of two writers' ideas and attitudes, you need to compare:

- what they are writing about: the **topic** of their text
- the writer's **ideas and attitudes** about the topic of their text
- the writers' **intentions**: the impact they want to have on the reader.

① Complete the sentences below to summarise the key similarities and differences in the two texts, the writers' ideas and attitudes, and their intentions. ✏️

A. Comparing topics

Both texts are about ....

....

....

However in Source A ....

....

....

whereas in Source B ....

....

....

B. Comparing ideas and opinions

Both writers think that ....

....

....

However in Source A ....

....

....

whereas in Source B ....

....

....

C. Comparing intentions

Both writers want their readers to ....

....

....

However in Source A ....

....

....

whereas in Source B ....

....

....

2 How do I develop my comparison of ideas and attitudes?

To develop your comparison of the writer's ideas and attitudes, you need to explore **how** they are conveyed.

① Look closely at four key quotations from **Source A** and from **Source B** below.

Source A: Eothen

A.
Familiar to one from the days of early childhood... they were just as I had always known them.

B.
the bigness of the distinct blocks of stones was the first sign by which I attained to feel the immensity of the whole pile.

C.
a cold sense and understanding of the Pyramid's enormity came down, overcasting my brain.

D.
When I was very young I was often in time of night the victim of a strange kind of mental oppression.

Source B: The Lost Continent

A.
No matter how many times you read about it or see it pictured, it still takes your breath away.

B.
a deep, inexpressible awe that anything on this earth could be so vast, so beautiful

C.
I was a particularly talkative and obnoxious child, but it stopped me cold.

D.
It is ten miles across, a mile deep, 180 miles long.

Can you spot any similarities or differences in the way that each writer conveys their ideas and attitudes in the quotations above?

a Circle Ⓐ **one** of the boxed words in each of the sentences below to sum up any similarities or differences you have spotted.

			Source A Quote	Source B Quote
Both	One	of the writers describe(s) their feelings.		
Both	One	of the writers has/have seen this place many times before.		
Both	One	of the writers talk(s) about their childhood.		
Both	One	of the writers use(s) facts and statistics.		

b Choose a quote from each of the texts above as evidence to support your answers.
Write ✏ the letter of your chosen quotations at the end of each sentence.

3 How do I structure my comparison?

When you write a comparison of the writers' ideas and attitudes in two texts, you need to:
- identify a similarity or difference in the writers' ideas and attitudes

and/or
- identify a similarity or difference in the ways in which they convey them

and
- closely analyse how they have used language and structure to convey them.

For more help with commenting on language and structure, see Units 3, 4 and 5.

(1) Look at the sentences below. They are from one paragraph of a student's response to this exam-style question.

Exam-style question

Compare how the writers have conveyed their different views and experiences of the places they describe.

Which of the sentences would you include in a paragraph comparing the two texts? Tick (✓) them.

Writing about both texts

A.
> Both writers describe a place and express the great impact that it has on them.

B.
> Source B explains how the Canyon was created but Source A does not explain how the Pyramids were built.

C.
> The writer of Source B uses facts whereas the writer of Source A uses a description of his personal experience of trying to climb the pyramid to highlight its size.

Writing about Source A

D.
> The writer of Source A says he has 'no print, no picture before me' but he recognises the famous pyramids immediately.

E.
> The writer describes how he 'came, and trod, and touched with my hands, and climbed' just to get to 'the top of one single stone'.

F.
> This emphasises how huge each stone in the pyramid is and so how much more enormous the whole pyramid is.

Writing about Source B

G.
> In Source B the writer uses lots of statistics, for example, 'ten miles across, a mile deep, 180 miles long' and comparisons with the Empire State Building and the whole of Manhattan.

H.
> This list of facts and comparisons suggests the writer is struggling to find a number or an idea that fully conveys just how vast the Grand Canyon really is.

(2) Number (✎) the sentences you have ticked to show how you would sequence them in a paragraph.

Comparing ideas and attitudes

An effective comparison focuses on the writers' ideas and attitudes **and** how they are conveyed.

Look at this exam-style question you saw at the start of the unit.

Exam-style question

Compare how the writers have conveyed their different views and experiences of the places they describe.

(1) Now look at the paragraph below, written by a student in response to this exam-style question.

> Both writers try to describe the experience of seeing an amazing place: the pyramids in Source A and the Grand Canyon in Source B. The writer of Source B describes how when he was a 'talkative and obnoxious child', the sight of the Grand Canyon 'stopped me cold'. Highlighting how he was 'talkative' but was silenced by the canyon emphasises the impact it can have even on a child. The writer of Source A, however, describes a strange dream he had as a child but then the impact of the pyramids is described more immediately as he feels it 'fill and load my mind'. The word 'fill' suggests there is no room for anything else in his mind while the word 'load' helps to convey the hugeness and heaviness of the pyramid itself and its effect on the writer. Both texts focus on their personal experience to convey the great impact of these places.

a Annotate the paragraph, underlining Ⓐ and labelling 🖉 where in the paragraph this student has achieved the key features listed below.

A. Identifies a similarity or difference in the two writers' ideas and attitudes.

B. Supports with a quotation or textual reference from Source B.

C. Analyses the impact of the quotation from Source B.

D. Supports with a quotation or textual reference from Source A.

E. Analyses the impact of the quotation from Source A.

F. Compares how the two writers have conveyed their ideas and attitudes and/or compares the impact of the writers' choices on the reader.

b How could this student improve the paragraph above? Write 🖉 a sentence or two summarising your ideas.

....

....

....

....

Your turn!

You are now going to write your own answer in response to the exam-style question.

Exam-style question

For this question, you need to refer to the **whole of source** A together with the **whole of source B**.

Compare how the writers have conveyed their different views and experiences of the places they describe.

In your answer, you could:

- compare their different views and experiences
- compare the methods they use to convey those views and experiences
- support your ideas with quotations from both texts.

(16 marks)

(1) You should spend 20–25 minutes on this kind of question, so should aim to write ✐ three or four paragraphs. Use the space below to plan three paragraphs.

	Similarity or differences	Source 1: Evidence	Source 2: Evidence
1			
2			
3			

(2) Now write ✐ your response to the exam-style question above on paper.

Review your skills

Check up

Review your response to the exam-style question on page 63. Tick ✓ the column to show how well you think you have done each of the following.

	Not quite ✓	Nearly there ✓	Got it! ✓
identified and compared similarities and differences in the writers' ideas and attitudes	☐	☐	☐
analysed and compared how the writers convey their ideas and attitudes	☐	☐	☐
structured my comparison of the writers' ideas and attitudes	☐	☐	☐

Need more practice?

Here is another exam-style question, this time relating to Source B on page 74, an extract from *The Private Diary of the Master of a London Ragged School* and Source C on page 75 *A Back Seat Education*, a newspaper article published in 2016. You'll find some suggested points to refer to in the Answers section.

Exam-style question

For this question, you need to refer to the **whole of source B** together with the **whole of source C**.

Compare how the writers have conveyed their different attitudes to young people.

In your answer, you could:

- compare their different attitudes
- compare the methods they use to convey their attitudes
- support your ideas with quotations from both texts.

(16 marks)

How confident do you feel about each of these **skills?** Colour ✐ in the bars.

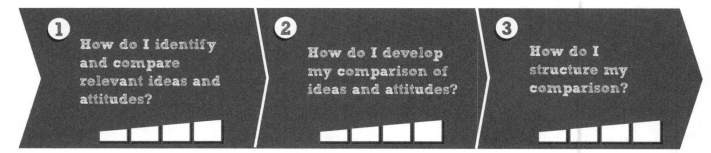

1 How do I identify and compare relevant ideas and attitudes?

2 How do I develop my comparison of ideas and attitudes?

3 How do I structure my comparison?

⑨ Expressing your ideas clearly and precisely

This unit will help you learn how to express your ideas clearly and precisely. The skills you will build are to:

- select vocabulary to express your ideas precisely
- link your ideas to express them clearly
- extend your sentences to develop ideas more fully.

In the exam you will face questions like the one below. This is about the text on page 66. At the end of the unit you will write your own response to this question.

Exam-style question

You now need to refer **only** to **Source 1** about a snake at a zoo.

How does the writer use language to describe his experience at the zoo?   **(12 marks)**

Before you tackle the question you will work through three key questions in the **skills boosts** to help you express your ideas clearly and precisely.

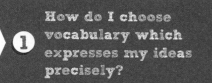

① How do I choose vocabulary which expresses my ideas precisely?

② How can I link my ideas to express them more clearly?

③ How can I extend my sentences to develop my ideas more fully?

Read the extract on page 66 from *The Zoo* by E F Benson, published in 1894. You will tackle a 19th century non-fiction extract in the Reading section of your Paper 2 exam.

As you read, remember the following: ✓

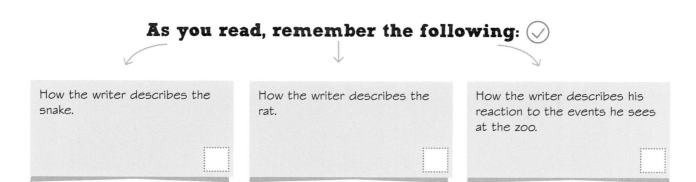

How the writer describes the snake.

How the writer describes the rat.

How the writer describes his reaction to the events he sees at the zoo.

The writer describes his encounter with a snake in London Zoo.

Source 1 The Zoo, E F Benson 🖉

It is possible to catch a snake's eye. He will not look at you for long, but in one second of that glance you will get to know something of the eternal mystery of evil, which you will scarcely learn elsewhere.

I cannot think of him as an animal, he is evil, no more. I once saw the snakes fed; the public are no longer allowed to see it, and quite rightly. There were about a dozen people in the snakehouse, at the time, and I think we were
5 all silent as we went out, when the feeding was over. The snake I watched was a large python from South America. I cannot remember his name, and I have never been near the cage since - and he was given a live rat, for they will not eat the dead food. The rat was let in through a small wire grating, and seemed quite at his ease at first, for the snake was asleep. He ran about the cage for a little while, and eventually walked across two of the reptile's coils. At that moment the other opened his eyes and saw the rat. He was in no hurry, and stretched himself slowly.
10 That was the most awful motion I ever saw; though the head and the end of the tail of the beast remained still, the great coils stirred and glided along one another, parallel lines moved in opposite directions, and passed and repassed silently and smoothly.

The rat was still unconcerned, he was sitting in a corner, performing his last **toilet**, which was not worth while, and it was very pitiful. Presently he looked up, and saw that which made him drop down on all-fours, and tremble.

15 The snake had fully awoke, he was hungry and it was dinner time; two small eyes were looking towards the living meal… it was horrible.

It is many years since I saw that sight. It was, I think, the most terrifying thing I ever beheld. In sleep, the horror of it sometimes still reaches me. I am in a dim unfamiliar room, alone at first, but as I sit there, something wakes into existence which is horrible, evil, not understood, and I cannot get away.

toilet: washing and grooming itself

1 How do I choose vocabulary which expresses my ideas precisely?

When writing about a text, you need to choose vocabulary which is appropriately formal and expresses your ideas as clearly and precisely as possible.

1 Look at some possible vocabulary choices to describe the snake in the extract on page 66.

In this extract the snake is depicted as…

| evil | | bad | | unpleasant | | dangerous | | | |
| deadly | | mean | | nasty | | hungry | | | |

a Add ✎ two more possible vocabulary choices in the blank spaces.

b Which vocabulary choice describes your impression of the snake most accurately? Tick ✓ it.

c Write ✎ a sentence explaining your choice.

2 Look at this quotation.

Presently he looked up, and saw that which made him drop down on all-fours, and tremble.

Now look at an analysis of the quotation and some possible vocabulary choices that you could use to complete it. Choose the clearest, most precise vocabulary choices to fill the blanks. ✎

suggest
imply
create the
impression
make me think
mean

The verbs 'drop' and 'tremble' ....

that the rat is ....

both
neither
extremely
rather
slightly

shocked
surprised
stunned
paralysed
startled

and
yet
or
nor
but

terrified
petrified
worried
nervous
frightened

3 Look again at the final paragraph of the extract.

a Note down ✎ **four** possible vocabulary choices to describe the impact that these events had on the writer.

b Tick ✓ the **two** vocabulary choices that you think are most precise and accurate.

2 How can I link my ideas to express them more clearly?

Conjunctions can link your ideas, making them more clearly and fluently expressed.

Coordinating conjunctions, such as:

| and | but | or | so |

can join related or contrasting ideas.

Subordinating conjunctions express more complex connections such as:

- an explanation e.g. because in order to
- a condition e.g. if unless
- a comparison e.g. although whereas
- a sequence e.g. when before until

① Compare these sentences from student answer A with single sentences B and C.

A.
> The description of the snake and the rat is horrible. The writer's description of his nightmare at the end of the extract is even more disturbing.

B.
> The description of the snake and the rat is horrible but the writer's description of his nightmare at the end of the extract is even more disturbing.

C.
> Although the description of the snake and the rat is horrible, the writer's description of his nightmare at the end of the extract is even more disturbing.

a Which version is expressed most clearly and fluently? Tick ✓ it.

b Write ✏ a sentence explaining your choice.

....

....

....

....

② Rewrite ✏ the sentences below into single sentences using a conjunction to make each one's meaning clearer and its expression more fluent. Remember to adjust the punctuation.

A.
> The description of the snake 'looking towards the living meal' is repulsive. The writer does not go on to describe the snake actually eating it.

....

....

....

B.
> The writer makes clear his opinion of snakes. He describes them as 'evil' at the beginning of his account.

....

....

....

How can I extend my sentences to develop my ideas more fully?

You can extend your sentences by linking related ideas in a number of different ways.

One way is to use a present participle: the verb form that ends in *-ing*. For example:

| The writer makes clear his opinion of snakes. | + | He describes them as 'evil' at the beginning of his account. | = | The writer makes clear his opinion of snakes, describing them as 'evil' at the beginning of his account. |

The present participle 'describing' clearly and fluently links these two points.

1. Present participles are the form of a verb that ends in *-ing*. Complete the table below, adding the present participles of these three verbs. The first one has been done to help you.

Verb	Present participle
build	building
list	
point	
suggest	

2. Rewrite the two sentences below, using a present participle to create a single sentence.

| The writer gives a long description of everything the rat does when it enters the cage. | + |

| The writer builds up to the terrifying moment when the snake stares at its 'living meal'. | = |

....

....

....

....

....

3. You can add a range of detailed information to sentences using a number of present participles. How could you use present participles to link these **four** ideas into a single sentence? Write your sentence below

| The writer presents the rat as the snake's helpless victim. |

| The writer lists what the rat does. | | The writer points out that the rat is 'at his ease at first'. |

| This suggests that the rat has no idea of the danger he is in. |

....

....

....

....

....

Expressing your ideas clearly and precisely

To express your ideas as clearly and precisely as possible, you need to think about:

- selecting the most precise vocabulary
- sinking and extending your ideas using conjunctions and/or present participles.

Now look at this exam-style question you saw at the start of the unit.

Exam-style question

How does the writer use language to describe his experience at the zoo?

(1) Look at a short paragraph from one student's response to the task.

> The writer's description of the snake waking up is horrible. He describes it as 'the most awful motion I ever saw'. He uses the words 'stirred and glided' and the words 'silently and smoothly.' This suggests that that the animal is sneaky and dangerous. He creates the feeling that something bad is going to happen.

a Underline (A) three examples of vocabulary which could be more precise.

b Note (✎) down in the margin **at least three** alternative vocabulary choices for each one.

c Mark (✎) any of the sentences which you feel should be linked or developed to improve the clarity and precision of the writing.

d Write (✎) an improved version of this paragraph, either by adjusting the text above or by rewriting it in the space below.

....
....
....
....
....
....
....
....

Your turn!

You are now going to write just **one** paragraph in response to this exam-style question.

Exam-style question

You now need to refer **only** to **Source 1** about a snake at a zoo.

How does the writer use language to describe his experience at the zoo? **(12 marks)**

In your exam, you should spend around 15 minutes on this type of question and write three or four paragraphs. However, you are now going to write just **one** paragraph. This will allow you to focus more closely on expressing your ideas as clearly and precisely as possible.

1. Look at some of the features of the extract on page 66 which contribute to showing the narrator's fear.

Feature	Quotation
The writer describes the snake:	in one second of that glance you will get to know something of the eternal mystery of evil
	He was in no hurry, and stretched himself slowly. That was the most awful motion I ever saw
	the great coils stirred and glided along one another, parallel lines moved in opposite directions, and passed and repassed silently and smoothly.
	two small eyes were looking towards the living meal… it was horrible.
The writer describes the rat:	The rat was still unconcerned, he was sitting in a corner, performing his last toilet, which was not worth while, and it was very pitiful.
	Presently he looked up, and saw that which made him drop down on all-fours, and tremble.
The writer describes his and others' response to the feeding:	the public are no longer allowed to see it
	we were all silent as we went out
	the most terrifying thing I ever beheld.
	something wakes into existence which is horrible, evil, not understood, and I cannot get away.

a. Choose **one** ⊘ of the features above which you can explore in your response to the exam-style question.

b. Use your chosen feature and at least one quotation to write ✎ a paragraph on paper in response to the exam-style question. Remember to:
- choose your vocabulary carefully
- think about ways in which you can link your ideas to express them clearly and precisely.

Review your skills

Check up

Review your response to the exam-style question on page 71. Tick ✓ the column to show how well you think you have done each of the following.

	Not quite ✓	Nearly there ✓	Got it! ✓
selected precise vocabulary	☐	☐	☐
linked my ideas clearly and precisely with conjunctions	☐	☐	☐
linked my ideas clearly and precisely with present participles	☐	☐	☐

Look over all of your work in this unit. Note down ✏ the three most important things to remember when trying to express your ideas as clearly and precisely as possible.

1. ....

2. ....

3. ....

Need more practice?

You can EITHER:

① Look again at your paragraph written in response to the exam-style question on page 71. Rewrite it ✏, experimenting with different vocabulary choices and sentence structures, linking your ideas in different ways. Which are most effective in expressing your ideas clearly and precisely?

AND/OR

② Choose a **second** point from the suggestions on page 71. Write ✏ a further paragraph in response to the exam-style question, focusing closely on your vocabulary choices and sentence structures.

How confident do you feel about each of these **skills**? Colour ✏ in the bars.

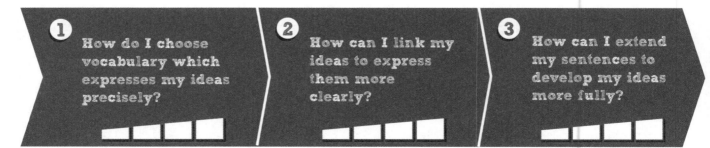

❶ How do I choose vocabulary which expresses my ideas precisely?

❷ How can I link my ideas to express them more clearly?

❸ How can I extend my sentences to develop my ideas more fully?

More practice texts

Nat, a farm worker, has noticed that the birds on the farm are behaving strangely.

Source A: The Birds, Daphne Du Maurier, 1893

Nat's bedroom faced east. He woke just after two and heard the wind in the chimney. Not the storm and bluster of a sou'westerly gale, bringing the rain, but east wind, cold and dry. It sounded hollow in the chimney, and a loose slate rattled on the roof. Nat listened, and he could hear the sea roaring in the bay. Even the air in the small bedroom had turned chill: A draft came under the skirting of the door, blowing upon the bed. Nat drew the blanket round him, leaned closer to the back of his sleeping wife, and stayed wakeful, watchful, aware of misgiving without cause.

Then he heard the tapping on the window. There was no creeper on the cottage walls to break loose and scratch upon the pane. He listened, and the tapping continued until, irritated by the sound, Nat got out of bed and went to the window. He opened it, and as he did so something brushed his hand, jabbing at his knuckles, grazing the skin. Then he saw the flutter of the wings and it was gone, over the roof, behind the cottage.

It was a bird; what kind of bird he could not tell. The wind must have driven it to shelter on the sill.

He shut the window and went back to bed but, feeling his knuckles wet, put his mouth to the scratch. The bird had drawn blood. Frightened, he supposed, and bewildered, the bird, seeking shelter, had stabbed at him in the darkness. Once more he settled himself to sleep.

Presently the tapping came again, this time more forceful, more insistent, and now his wife woke at the sound and, turning in the bed, said to him, "See to the window, Nat, it's rattling."

"I've already seen to it," he told her; "there's some bird there trying to get in. Can't you hear the wind? It's blowing from the east, driving the birds to shelter."

"Send them away," she said, "I can't sleep with that noise."

He went to the window for the second time, and now when he opened it, there was not one bird upon the sill but half a dozen; they flew straight into his face, attacking him.

He shouted, striking out at them with his arms, scattering them; like the first one, they flew over the roof and disappeared. Quickly he let the window fall and latched it.

"Did you hear that?" he said. "They went for me. Tried to peck my eyes." He stood by the window, peering into the darkness, and could see nothing. His wife, heavy with sleep, murmured from the bed.

"I'm not making it up," he said, angry at her suggestion. "I tell you the birds were on the sill, trying to get into the room."

Suddenly a frightened cry came from the room across the passage where the children slept.

"It's Jill," said his wife, roused at the sound, sitting up in bed. "Go to her, see what's the matter."

Nat lit the candle, but when he opened the bedroom door to cross the passage the draft blew out the flame.

There came a second cry of terror, this time from both children, and stumbling into their room, he felt the beating of wings about him in the darkness. The window was wide open. Through it came the birds, hitting first the ceiling and the walls, then swerving in midflight, turning to the children in their beds.

"It's all right, I'm here," shouted Nat, and the children flung themselves, screaming, upon him, while in the darkness the birds rose and dived and came for him again.

An anonymous teacher writes in his diary of 1850 about his first few days at a Ragged School. Ragged schools were charitable schools offering a free education to poor, inner-city children in the 19th century.

Source B: The Private Diary of the Master of a London Ragged School, 1850

Most of the children can read very well indeed. Some of them can write, and almost all of the first class can say the multiplication table well; they all promise to be expert at figures. In mere schooling they are not behindhand; but in decency of behaviour or in respect for the teacher, or in discipline of any kind, they are totally unparalleled. No school can be possibly worse than this.

* * * * *

I had occasion to punish a boy slightly this morning: he swore and blasphemed most horribly, and rushed from the school. I took little notice of this display, and sat down calmly to hear the class with which I was engaged read the Acts of the Apostles. I was suddenly startled by a large stone passing my ear. If it had struck me on the head, I must have been severely hurt. I got out of the reach of stones thrown through the window, and continued the lesson. Several followed-half-a-dozen at least. He was ready in the court with a brick in his hand, to have his revenge when I came out. With some difficulty I got out of the lane without being obliged to run. I considered it best to call at the police station, and ask for a **convoy**. This was readily granted; and followed at a short distance by the policeman, I returned to the school.

* * * * *

All our copy-books have been stolen, and proofs exist that the school is used at night as a sleeping-room. We must get a stronger door to it. I must also get a tub to stand by the pump in the court, and a piece of coarse towelling and soap. My duties must resolve themselves into —
First – To see the boys and girls well washed and scrubbed.
Secondly – To try to get prayers said decently.
Thirdly – To give them a lesson in their duties and privileges, for they have many, and know none.
Fourthly – Some religious instruction.
Fifthly – Reading.
Sixthly – Writing.
Seventhly – Arithmetic.

* * * * *

It is a sad thing to turn anyone out, but I have reluctantly determined to get rid for the present of three or four of the most unruly boys … I used the cane for the first time to-day, with effect. These children cannot be managed well without some use of it. What then is to be done? Am I to wait for order until they are capable of appreciating kindness? If so, I must wait a very long time. A little touch of the cane is the least injurious mode of punishment that can be adopted. It is over at once, and boy and master are not the worse friends for it. Were this a regular, **well-appointed** school, then my punishments, if needed, would be rare, but severe. Here no system can be adopted. Were I to punish some boy as he deserved, for the advantage of the rest, then my life would not be safe. Every boy, therefore, must stand alone. It is not a school, but a collection of poor ignorant outcasts, and they must be treated accordingly. They will not be managed by sheer force nor by kindness — a mixture of all kinds of legitimate **expedients** must be used.

convoy: a policeman to follow and protect him
well-appointed: having good facilities
expedients: methods

Author Marianne Levy describes her journey on a school bus to see whether things had changed in the two decades since she last went on a school bus.

Source C: A Back Seat Education, Marianne Levy, 2016

"I only like him about 30 per cent now. Which is way down from before, when I liked him 100 per cent."

"That's so many per cent, Ruby."

"I know."

Ever wondered what happens after you've dropped your teenager at the bus stop? As the nation's children returned for the January term, I decided to find out, and now I'm sitting on the back seat with the 4pm crowd, right between Ruby and her friend, my head swivelling to catch their words over the growl of the engine. I'm the most obvious undercover reporter ever. But I'm not wearing school uniform, and so, as far as they're concerned, I'm completely invisible.

A lot has happened in the couple of decades since I took the bus to school. But it's good to know that some things haven't really changed.

Though I am currently juddering across north London, my journey once took me from Chelmsford to Colchester and back. It was a 50-mile round trip. And it made *Lord of the Flies* look like a spa break. So when I was searching for a scary landscape into which to plunge the heroine of my new teen-fiction novel, there was no need to conjure up a vampire-ridden dystopia; I just had to travel back 20 years in my own head.

The discussion turns to whether or not Ali's shoes are Air Max ("Obviously they are not," says Ruby), and as we turn a corner, I stagger down towards the front to check in on a pair of tiny boys, apple-cheeked angels in blazers. The more cherubic of the two is spewing forth a stream of swearwords. His friend responds by bashing him over the head with a violin case. It's all reassuringly familiar, although I'm worried for the violin.

In my days of getting the bus, I wouldn't have given the safety of musical instruments a second thought; my entire focus was on self-preservation. Culled from four very different schools and trapped together for around 15 hours every week, we formed a strange, uneasy society.

There were adults, of course, but they ignored us. The bus driver, occasionally called upon to intervene after a particularly brutal fight, would inevitably refuse to get involved, saying gloomily (and probably correctly), "I'm not paid enough for this."

There were moments of genuine danger, too: the night my friend crossed in front of the bus and bounced off a Volvo through a lane of fast traffic; the time the sunroof caught a branch and flew off, leaving a square of night sky pouring cold air down on to our surprised heads.

Whole lifetimes' worth of social interaction could be condensed into a single journey; wars fought, bonds forged and loves lost while the double-decker idled in traffic on the Kelvedon slip road.

Do I miss it? Maybe, just a little. It was exhausting, the constant attack and defence, the emotional energy we'd expend on the most trivial arguments, the way any foodstuff might be turned into a missile. But then there were the frosty mornings when we'd send our breath up in warm white plumes and pretend we were holding cigarettes, the secrets shared over a flaking Curly Wurly as the top deck emptied, the friendships so intense they burned.

Back in London, the girls barge past me, and, as though to drive the point home, one actually stands on my foot as she reaches for the bell.

"See ya, Rubes," says her friend, swinging off on to the pavement. And Ruby settles down into her seat, pops her headphones into her ears, and flashes me a tiny, satisfied smile.

Answers

Unit 1

Page 3

1 **a** i. sashes (line 2): one section or panel of a sliding sash window

ii. cellar-flap (line 4): a trap door allowing entry to a cellar from outside a house

iii. modes (line 8): ways, methods

iv. secrete (line 16): hide

v. connive (line 24): to co-operate secretly in a dishonest activity

2 eg This is a non-fiction text about how burglars get into buildings, written to inform a reader who may not have been aware of the tricks that burglars use. The writer does not give any opinion about burglars or crime but presents the information without bias.

Page 4

1 Paragraph 1: How burglars get into houses.

Paragraph 2: How burglars deceive the police and servants.

Paragraph 3: How burglars get into and remove goods from warehouses.

2 eg Burglars undo window catches with a thin instrument; they climb over roofs and get in through trap-doors in the roof or an attic window; they break through walls from adjoining buildings; they climb up the waterspout to get in at a window.

3 eg They may not be able to get the cabman to connive at the theft; the number of the cab could be taken by a witness.

Page 5

1 The text aims to engage the reader's interest and develop their understanding.

2 **b** There is no obvious bias evident in the text. Readers are likely to consider an information text written without bias to be a reliable and trustworthy source.

Page 6

A, C, E and F are TRUE. The student who completed the task has scored only 3 marks, marking A, C and F as TRUE correctly and marking G as TRUE incorrectly.

Page 7

A, C, F and G are TRUE.

Page 8

Q	The Birds
	Read again the first part of the source, lines 1 to 11.
	List **four** things from this part of the text that Nat hears. **(4 marks)**

A	• the wind in the chimney
	• a loose slate rattling on the roof
	• the sea roaring in the bay
	• tapping on the window

Unit 2

Page 11

1/2. All are potentially valid choices.

Page 12

1 B/C. eg the repetition of 'baby' in negative terms emphasises the strangeness of the child; the use of plain, unemotional language and short sentences creates a blunt, emphatic tone.

D. The writer's choices suggest the narrator's (and characters') shock and dismay at the baby's appearance.

Page 13

1 **2** A is the longest response, but the least developed; B gives limited comment on word choice; C gives a detailed and specific comment on word and sentence structure choice so offers the most developed analysis.

3 May comment on the use of plain simple language suggesting an unemotional response to the baby, or the blunt minor sentence emphasising its surprising weight.

Page 14

1

quotation from the text	"'He's a funny little chap,' said David, and he sounded dismayed."
comments on vocabulary and/ or sentence structure choices	The word 'dismayed' suggests his disappointment. The phrase 'funny little chap' does not really sum up the baby described in the rest of the extract so it suggests this short sentence is the only thing the father can think of to say about him. It shows the tense silence in the room as the husband and wife look in shock at their baby.
comments precisely on the impact of these choices on readers	The description of the baby is very disturbing and even shocking for readers. The writer emphasises this in the father's reaction to the baby... The writer uses this reaction to create tension.
use key words from the question	description... baby... baby... described

(2) The paragraph is structured: explain-evidence-point-explain. The key idea to explore is that, while P-E-E can support students in developing their analytical skills, slavishly following it can limit analysis and, therefore, achievement.

Page 16

Q	*The Private Diary of the Master of a London Ragged School* Look in detail at lines 14 to 32 of the source. How does the writer use language to create an impression of the students in his school? **(8 marks)**
A	'well washed and scrubbed' suggests the students are very dirty the students know none of their 'duties and privileges' suggesting they are irresponsible and badly behaved 'unruly' further suggests poor behaviour in some of the students the master's worry that 'my life would not be safe" suggests that some students can be aggressive and violent

Unit 3

Page 19

(1) Frightened, upset.

(2) 2, 3, 5 and 6 suggest fear.

(3) **a** bewilderment, terror, towered, wept, knife-edged, wicked

(4) • "I wept" because it suggests the narrator is frightened and upset
  • "I didn't know where to move" because it suggests the narrator is paralysed with fear
  • "knife-edged, dark, and a wicked green" because it suggests he is even frightened of the grass
  • "screaming" because it suggests he is frightened of the birds and the noises they make

Page 20

(1) eg frightened, intimidated, threatened, abandoned

(2) sympathy
  b eg 'howled' shows he is upset; 'did not expect to be found again' suggests he feels abandoned

(3) **a** eg much happier, more settled
  b eg relieved
  c eg 'awakened', 'shields', 'grins'

Page 21

(1) **a b c** Suggests a distressed, wild animal; suggests narrator is distressed and wild with fear, encouraging the reader to understand how upset he is and therefore feel sympathy for him.

(2) **a b** Suggests the narrator is a victim of the sun's bullying bright light – more usually considered something positive – again creating sympathy.

Page 22

(1) Lines 1 to 20, language, describe, narrator's thoughts and feelings.

(2)

uses key words from the question	The writer describes... the narrator feels when he thinks... The writer uses language...
identifies the writer's intention	how upset and threatened the narrator feels
supported with evidence from the text	'It was knife-edged; dark, and a wicked green'
comments on connotations of language choices	the word 'knife-edged' makes it sound sharp and dangerous and threatening and the word 'wicked' makes it sound evil and like it is trying to harm him.
comments on how this helps to achieve the writer's intention	The writer uses language to make the reader feel sorry for the narrator because he is so young and he thinks he is in serious danger.

Page 24

Q	*The Birds* Look in detail at lines 14 to 23 of the source. How does the writer use language here to create a tense, frightening atmosphere? You could include the writer's choice of: • words and phrases • language features and techniques • sentence forms. **(8 marks)**
A	The short emphatic sentence 'The bird had drawn blood.' creates a shocking, dramatic moment of tension. Nat assumes the bird is 'Frightened... bewildered' suggesting that he is unaware of the danger he is in. The long sentence in the final paragraph of lines 14–23 builds tension slowly, first highlighting the growing number of birds, then their flight at him and, finally, the attack.

Unit 4

Page 27

(1) eg
'All over the country this month, GCSE pupils will be sitting down, once again, to slog through their exams. Whether it's the chorus of sniffing, the three hours of cramping fingers, the coldly sweating armpits or the hotly anticipated questions that never appear, exams are an archetypal stress dream for a reason.' But I'm afraid they matter. They matter enormously.

A/C 'But I'm afraid they matter. They matter enormously.'

B/C 'Whether it's the chorus of sniffing, the three hours of cramping fingers, the coldly sweating armpits or the hotly anticipated questions that never appear, exams are an archetypal stress dream for a reason.'

D/C 'All over the country this month, GCSE pupils will be sitting down, once again, to slog through their exams.'

② **a** The 'slog' of GCSEs

② **a** The 'slog' of GCSEs

b Delaying this idea to the end of the sentence, following the adverbials highlighting the number of people affected, gives it great emphasis.

Page 28

① eg

- Sentence A: 'All over the country this month, GCSE pupils will be sitting down, once again, to slog through their exams.' A longer sentence, highlighting a key idea, emphasises the hard work that GCSE students will experience.

- Sentence B: 'Whether it's the chorus of sniffing, the three hours of cramping fingers, the coldly sweating armpits or the hotly anticipated questions that never appear, exams are an archetypal stress dream for a reason.' A longer sentence, listing descriptive detail to highlight the problems and stress that GCSE students will face.

- Sentence C: 'But I'm afraid they matter. They matter enormously.' Short sentences, adding emphasis to highlight the importance of exams and so suggest the pressure which students experience.

Page 29

① **a** eg The writer uses lots of emotive language choices to describe the fear and anxiety of exams [D], such as 'cramping fingers… coldly sweating armpits' [B]. However some of the strongest key points are delivered using very blunt, simple language. [C] for example 'Exams are not the time for peer pressure' [A]. The writer structures this point in a short sentence to add emphasis [E] effectively highlighting the pressure that GCSE students are likely to experience. [F]

b G and H are least likely to form part of an effective analytical response.

Page 30

① Writer, language, experience, GCSE exams.

② Student B's response is the most effective. It features the most detailed analysis, clearly focused on the exam-style question.

Page 32

Q	A Back Seat Education
	You now need only to refer to Source C.
	How does the writer use language to describe her experience of travelling on the school bus when she was a student? **(12 marks)**
A	The phrase 'self-preservation' suggests a dangerous experience.
	The listing structure of 'wars fought, bonds forged and loves lost' succinctly summarises the emotional and physical danger and drama of these journeys.
	Detailed descriptive language builds vivid, evocative images of eg 'a square of night sky pouring cold air down on to our surprised heads', 'we'd send our breath up in warm white plumes and pretend we were holding cigarettes'.
	The contrast of 'attack and defence', 'arguments' and 'friendships so intense' emphasises the extreme nature of the school bus journeys.

Unit 5

Page 35

① The correct order of key elements:

B. Level is leaving his home land.

G. The writer describes Lev.

A. Lev puts a cigarette in his mouth.

D. A woman tells him he is not allowed to smoke on the coach.

C. Lev imagines having to sit next to the woman on the long journey ahead.

F. Lev imagines his life in the United Kingdom.

E. Lev imagines the long journey ahead.

② - **Characters**: B, G, F, E contribute to the reader's impressions of the character of Lev.

- **Dialogue**: D contributes to the reader's impression of the character of Lev.

- **Events**: E contributes to the reader's impression of the character of Lev.

- **Settings**: B, F contribute to our impressions of Lev's old and new lives.

- **Mood**: All the elements contribute to the mood of the extract.

② The majority of the extract focuses on

- developing (and interesting the reader in) the character of Lev

- encouraging the reader to compare his old life with his expectations of his new life.

Page 36

① A, B, E

② A is achieved through character description, dialogue, events, setting

B is achieved through character description, setting, events

E is achieved through character description, setting, events

③ eg What will happen when Lev reaches the UK? Will Lev's new life exceed his expectations or be yet more disappointing? How will he respond in either case?

Page 37

① a/b. All could, arguably, be included in an effective analysis of the writer's structural choices.

Page 38

effective choice of quotation and reference to the text	The writer begins the novel with a journey… The writer describes 'fields of sunflowers' and 'pig farms' but does not really describe how he imagines London
identifies the writer's intention	it feels like the reader will be making the journey with him from his own country to the UK by coach.
analyses the impact of the writer's use of structure	There is a big difference between his life in his own country and the new life he imagines.

analyses the impact of the extract as the opening of a novel	so the reader can expect the shock he will have when he arrives in Britain and will want to find out what happens and how he deals with it.
focuses the analysis on the question	This is the main way the writer interests the reader, by getting us to take a journey into the unknown with Lev.

Page 40

Q	The Birds
	This text is from near the beginning of a short story.
	How has the writer structured the text to interest you as a reader?
	You could write about:
	• what the writer focuses your attention on at the beginning
	• how and why the writer changes this focus as the extract develops
	• any other structural features that interest you.
	(8 marks)
A	The beginning of the extract focuses on weather. This creates both an unsettling, disturbing atmosphere but also misleads Nat who assumes it is this which is making the birds behave strangely.
	Both Nat and his wife are unaware of the threat that the birds pose. Nat blames the weather; his wife thinks the window is rattling. This makes the shock of the attack all the more dramatic.
	The threat rapidly grows as the number of birds increases and they then attack the children.

Unit 6

Page 43

(2) The most explicit suggestion of Ugwu's feelings is towards the end of the extract where the writer describes his desire to be back at home, suggesting anxiety and uncertainty.

(3) (4) Each of these elements arguably suggests Ugwu's feelings.

- *Ugwu wonders if his aunty can feel the street getting hotter through her shoes* could suggest his discomfort and anxiety.
- *Ugwu mouthes the word 'street'* could suggest his excitement at being in a new place.
- *He smells sweet flowers in the university compound* could suggest excitement at the life of relative luxury he is beginning.
- *Ugwu agrees he will learn his new duties quickly* suggests his happiness to work hard and accept the pressure he is under to do so.
- *The narrator describes Ugwu's good fortune in being offered his new job* emphasises the pressure he may feel to work hard.
- *Ugwu stares at the car in the garage* suggests his excitement at his new surroundings.

- *Ugwu will always answer 'Yes, sah!'* suggests his happiness to work hard and accept the pressure he is under to do so.
- *Ugwu stops himself touching the cement wall* suggests his excitement and anxiety at the new life he is beginning.
- *Ugwu wishes he was back in his village* suggests anxiety and discomfort.

Page 44

(1) (a) eg sympathy, annoyance, admiration.

(b) eg

- The verb form suggests the pressure which Ugwu's aunty is placing upon him which could create sympathy or annoyance in the reader.
- The adjectives suggest again the pressure he is under.
- 'attentively' suggests Ugwu's acceptance of this pressure which could create admiration or sympathy in the reader.

Page 45

(1) (2) eg

- The writer's use of a short sentence in Ugwu's dialogue and the verb 'will' effectively emphasises Ugwu's determination and his obedience, creating sympathy and admiration in the reader.
- Ugwu's unquestioning repetition of 'Yes, sah!' suggests his willingness to obey his aunty and his new employer, encouraging the reader's sympathy and perhaps leading the reader to question whether a thirteen year old boy should be working as a servant.
- The contrast of an everyday object such as a cement wall and Ugwu's reluctance to touch it suggests how fascinated and impressed he is with the trappings of his new life but, at the same time, wary of behaving inappropriately.

Page 46

uses key words from the question	The writer suggests the feeling
evidence from the text	'often… how his good fortune came about'.
comments on vocabulary and/ or sentence form choices	The phrase 'good fortune' suggests how lucky Ugwu is to have got this job and the adverb 'often' emphasises that Ugwu's aunty wants him to appreciate how lucky he has been.
comments on how this helps to achieve the writer's intention	The writer does not say that Ugwu feels upset or annoyed by this pressure which suggests to me that he accepts it and understands what is expected of him.
comments on the impact of the text on the reader	
uses evaluative language to comment on the writer's success in achieving her intention	In this way the writer effectively suggests the pressure and Ugwu's feelings about it.

Page 48

Q	The Birds
	Focus this part of your answer on the second half of the source, from **line 22 to the end**.
	A student, having read this section of the text said: 'The writer makes this attack really shocking and frightening. It makes me want to find out why the birds are attacking and what will happen next.'
	To what extent do you agree?
	In your response, you could:
	• consider your own impressions of the attack and of the family's reactions
	• evaluate how the writer creates a shocking and frightening atmosphere
	• support your opinions with quotations from the text.
	(20 marks)
A	The growing number of birds suggests their unnatural, aggressive behaviour and reflects a growing threat.
	Nat's wife's reaction builds tension as does not recognise the threat.
	This is suddenly contrasted with the screams of their children, making the threat very real.
	The wind blows out the candle, adding to the sense of danger and threat.
	The 'cry of terror' and 'the beating of wings' in the darkness creates a frightening image.

Unit 7

Page 51

① ②

- Similarities:
  - o both texts focus on family
  - o both texts focus on a difficult relationship.
- Significant differences include:
  - o the narrator of Source A focuses on his grandfather's peculiarities while the writer of Source B focuses on a reconciliation between mother and son
  - o in Source A, the grandfather is the victim of his physical deterioration while in Source B the writer presents the mother and son as the victims of the son's 'dissolute connections'.

Page 52

①

Source A

A: suggests the narrator does not have fond memories of his grandfather.

E: suggests the narrator sees his grandfather as a source of humour.

B: suggests the narrator has a rather heartless attitude to his grandfather's infirmity.

Source B

A: suggests the woman's sadness at her son's situation and his coldness to her.

B: suggests the woman has always put her son's needs above her own.

C: suggests the boy is ungrateful to his mother.

D/E: suggests the boy is not as hard-hearted or as independent as he first appears.

② a b

Neither of the relationships seems very affectionate: A, B

One of the relationships is very strong: Source B, E

Both of the relationships show some unkindness: Source D, C

One of the relationships changes in the extract: Source B, C, E

Page 53

①
A, B, E and F all focus on family relationships and so are relevant. C and D focus on description in the texts and are therefore not directly relevant to the exam-style question.

② eg

- Both texts describe a difficult relationship, however Source A shows a relationship which is strange and distant whereas Source B shows a strong family bond overcoming difficulties.
- Source A focuses on the problems that the grandfather's old age caused, mainly for the rest of the family. Source B, on the other hand, focuses on the problems that young people can cause their families.

Page 54

The response does achieve A and B, but not C: no evidence is provided to support the comment on Source A.

Page 56

Q	Source B: The Private Diary of the Master of a London Ragged School and Source C: A Back Seat Education
	You need to refer to source B and source C for this question. Use details from both sources. Write a summary of the different situations the young people are in.
	Use evidence from both texts to support your answer. (8 marks)
A	Both texts suggest young people can be violent. In Source B, the master fears 'my life would not be safe' and in Source C, the writer describes one student 'bashing' another 'over the head with a violin case.'
	Both texts show young people swearing. In Source B, the master describes a boy who 'swore and blasphemed most horribly'. In Source C, the writer describes a boy 'spewing forth a stream of swearwords'.
	Both texts show young people disregarding adults. In Source B, the master writes about how they have no 'respect for the teacher'. In Source C, the writer says she is 'completely invisible' to the students on the bus.

Unit 8

Page 59

① eg:

A. Both texts are about visiting extraordinary places. However, in Source A the writer focuses on the pyramids, whereas in Source B the writer describes the Grand Canyon.

B. Both writers think that their chosen topic is an incredible place. However in Source A the writer tries to describe how he felt when he saw the pyramids whereas in Source B the writer concentrates on conveying the scale of the Grand Canyon.

C. Both writers want their readers to appreciate the size and power of the place they have visited. However, in Source A the writer wants the reader to understand the impact that the pyramids had on him whereas in Source B, the writer wants the reader to appreciate the impact of the Grand Canyon on everyone who sees it.

Page 60

(1) Both of the writers describe their feelings: B, C.

Both of the writers have seen this place many times before: A.

Both of the writers talk about their childhood: A, D.

One of the writers uses facts and statistics: D.

Page 61

(1) (2) eg

A. Both writers describe a place and express the great impact that it has on them.

H. In Source B the writer uses lots of statistics, for example, 'ten miles across, a mile deep, 180 miles long' and comparisons with the Empire State Building and the whole of Manhattan.

I. This list of facts and comparisons suggests the writer is struggling to find a number or an idea that fully conveys just how vast the Grand Canyon really is.

C. The writer of Source B uses facts whereas the writer of Source A uses a description of his personal experience of trying to climb the pyramid to highlight its size.

E. The writer describes how he 'came, and trod, and touched with my hands, and climbed' just to get to 'the top of one single stone'.

F. This emphasises how huge each stone in the pyramid is and so how much more enormous the whole pyramid is.

Page 62

(2) (a)

identifies a similarity or difference in the two writers' ideas and attitudes	Both writers try to describe the experience of seeing an amazing place: the pyramids in Source A and the Grand Canyon in Source B.
supports with a quotation or textual reference from Source B	The writer of Source B describes how when he was a 'talkative and obnoxious child', the sight of the Grand Canyon 'stopped me cold'.
analyses the impact of the quotation from Source B	Highlighting how he was 'talkative' but was silenced by the canyon emphasises the impact it can have even on a child.
supports with a quotation or textual reference from Source A	The writer of Source A, however, describes a strange dream he had as a child but then the impact of the pyramids is described more immediately as he feels it 'fill and load my mind'.
analyses the impact of the quotation from Source A	The word 'fill' suggests there is no room for anything else in his mind while the word 'load' helps to convey the hugeness and heaviness of the pyramid itself and its effect on the writer.
compares how the two writers have conveyed their ideas and attitudes and/or compares the impact of the writers' choices on the reader	Both texts focus on their personal experience to convey the great impact of these places.

(b) The final comparison of the ways in which the writers convey their ideas could be more fully developed, eg contrasting the use of humour in Source B with the strangely disturbing nightmare described in Source A.

Page 64

| Q | Source B: The Private Diary of the Master of a London Ragged School and Source C: A Back Seat Education

For this question, you need to refer to the **whole of source B** together with the **whole of source C**.

Compare how the writers have conveyed their different attitudes to young people.

In your answer, you could:
• compare their different attitudes
• compare the methods they use to convey their attitudes
• support your ideas with quotations from both texts.

(16 marks) |
|---|---|
| A | Both writers are sympathetic to young people. In Source B, the master 'reluctantly' expels one student and resolves to treat the others with a mixture of 'sheer force' and 'kindness'; in Source C, the writer remembers relationships on her school bus as 'exhausting' but she also remembers 'friendships so intense they burned'.

Neither writer condemns young people for their behaviour but seems to accept that young people can behave poorly. In Source B, the master focuses on improving his students' behaviour, 'to give them a lesson in their duties and privileges'; in Source C the writer thinks one student 'bashing' another with a violin case is 'reassuringly familiar' and seems more 'worried for the violin'.

However, in Source A the master describes his intention to use force to correct his students' behaviour using the cane which, he believes, is 'the least injurious mode of punishment'. The writer of Source C, however, simply observes and describes the students' behaviour with no intention to correct or improve it. |

Unit 9

Page 67

(1) (a) eg cruel, ruthless

(b) "deadly" and "dangerous" are arguably the most precise and formal choices given.

(2) eg the verbs 'drop' and 'tremble' <u>create the impression</u> that the rat is <u>both</u> <u>shocked and</u> <u>terrified</u>.

(3) eg disturbed, unsettled, upset, traumatised, horrified.

Page 68

(1) C is arguably the most fluently, and sophisticatedly, expressed.

(2) eg

A <u>Although</u> the description of the snake "looking towards the living meal" is repulsive, the writer does not go on to describe the snake actually eating it.

B The writer makes clear his opinion of snakes <u>when</u> he describes them as "evil" at the beginning of his account.

Page 69

(1) build/building; list/listing; point/pointing; suggest/suggesting.

(2) The writer gives a long description of everything the rat does when it enters the cage, <u>building</u> up to the terrifying moment when the snake stares at its 'living meal'.

(3) **Note** that these non-finite clauses, using present participles, are moveable within the sentence, eg

The writer presents the rat as the snake's helpless victim, listing what the rat does and pointing out that the rat is 'at his ease at first', suggesting that the rat has no idea of the danger he is in.

OR

The writer, listing what the rat does and pointing out that the rat is 'at his ease at first', presents the rat as the snake's helpless victim, suggesting that the rat has no idea of the danger he is in.

Page 70

(1) eg

The writer's description of the snake waking up is <u>repulsive</u>. He describes it as 'the most awful motion I ever saw', <u>using</u> the <u>verbs</u> 'stirred and glided' and the <u>adverbs</u> 'silently and smoothly' <u>in order to</u> <u>suggest</u> that it moves quickly and quietly <u>and</u> that the animal is <u>stealthy</u> and <u>deadly.</u> He <u>creates</u> the <u>impression</u> that something <u>terrible</u> is going to happen.

Published by Pearson Education Limited, 80 Strand, London, WC2R ORL.

www.pearsonschoolsandfecolleges.co.uk

Text © Pearson Education Limited 2016
Produced and typeset by Tech-Set Ltd, Gateshead
Original illustrations © Pearson Education Ltd 2016

The right of David Grant to be identified as author of this work has been asserted by him in accordance with the Copyright, Designs and Patents Act 1988.

First published 2016

19 18 17 16
10 9 8 7 6 5 4 3 2 1

British Library Cataloguing in Publication Data
A catalogue record for this book is available from the British Library

ISBN 978 0435 18319 6

Printed in Italy by Lego S.p.A

We are grateful to the following for permission to reproduce copyright material:

Extract on page 10 from *The Fifth Child* by Doris Lessing, Jonathan Cape, 1988, Reprinted by permission of HarperCollins Publishers Ltd. © Doris Lessing 1988 and Featured by kind permission of Jonathan Clowes Ltd., London, on behalf of The Estate of Doris Lessing; Extract on page 18 from *Cider with Rosie* by Laurie Lee, Published by Chatto & Windus, Reprinted by permission of The Random House Group Limited; Extract on page 26 adapted from How to survive the exam season by Nell Frizzell, *The Guardian*, 05/05/2015, Copyright © Guardian News and Media Ltd. 2016; Extract on page 34 from *The Road Home* by Rose Tremain, Published by Chatto & Windus, Reprinted by permission of The Random House Group Limited and Copyright © 2007 by Rose Tremain, Used by permission of Little, Brown and Company; Extract on page 42 from *Half of a Yellow Sun* by Chimamanda Ngozi Adichie, Harper Perennial, 2007, Reprinted by permission of HarperCollins Publishers Ltd. © Chimamanda Ngozi Adichie 2006 and Used by permission of Alfred A. Knopf, an imprint of the Knopf Doubleday Publishing Group, a division of Penguin Random House LLC. All rights reserved. Any third-party use of this material, outside of this publication, is prohibited. Interested parties must apply directly to Penguin Random House LLC for permission; Extract on page 50 from *Unreliable Memoirs* by Clive James, pub. Picador, London © Clive James 2008, with permission from Macmillan and Copyright © 2009, 1980 by Clive James. Used by permission of W. W. Norton & Company, Inc.; Extract on page 58 from *The Lost Continent* by Bill Bryson, Published by Transworld, Reprinted by permission of The Random House Group Limited and Brief excerpts from pp. 235, 237 from *The Lost Continent: Travels in Small-Town America* by Bill Bryson. Copyright © 1989 by Bill Bryson. Reprinted by permission of HarperCollins Publishers and Copyright © 1989 Bill Bryson. Reprinted by permission of Doubleday Canada, a division of Penguin Random House Canada Limited; Extract on page 73 from *The Birds* by Daphne Du Maurier, Penguin, 1952, Reproduced with permission of Curtis Brown Group Ltd. London on behalf of The Chichester Partnership. Copyright © The Chichester Partnership 1952; Extract on page 75 from A Back Seat Education by Marianne Levy, *The Independent*, 16/01/2016, Reproduced with permission.